P9-DCZ-782

VANISHING WILDLIFE *of* TEXAS

VANISHING

WILDLIFE of TEXAS
By John & Gloria Tveten
Illustrated by Gamini Ratnavira
ENDANGERED SPECIES
MEDIA PROJECT

Library of Congress Cataloging-in-Publication Data

Tveten, John L.
Vanishing wildlife of Texas / John & Gloria Tveten ;
Illustrations by Gamani Ratnavira

ISBN 0-9667142-0-2

1. Endangered species—-Texas. I. Tveten, Gloria A., 1938-
II. Title.
QL. 84.22.T4T83 1998 591.68\'920974 98-87616

Printed in the United States of America

Editing: Celia G. Homer
Production: Charlie Cardenas, Amy Kruger, Allen Duhon, Celia G. Homer
Cover paintings: Gamini Ratnavira

Published in the United States by
ENDANGERED SPECIES MEDIA PROJECT
1813 Missouri, Houston, TX 77006-2324
(713) 520-1985 Fax: (713) 529-1183
Web Site: www.neosoft.com/~esmp *E-mail*: esmp@neosoft.com

member of

Portions of the proceeds from the sale of this book go directly to *The Nature Conservancy of Texas*, the *Audubon Foundation of Texas* and the *International Crane Foundation*.

Earth Share
OF TEXAS

Printed on recycled paper

The Endangered Species

Media Project

dedicates this book

to the memory of

Army and Sarah Emmott

whose selfless efforts

on behalf of the

conservation community

will continue encouraging

Texans to preserve

the beauty and value

of our natural heritage

for generations to come

Recently at dawn in late March, I had the privilege of experiencing 14 male Attwater's Prairie Chickens displaying on their "booming grounds" on a pasture near Texas City. Suddenly a peregrine falcon circled the area. The chickens crouched motionless in the grass and escaped attack. After about an hour, the males resumed their efforts to attract females and perpetuate the fragile cycle of life. All the while, the distant background roar of traffic remained a solemn reminder that mankind poses the most serious of threats to Texas' vanishing wildlife.

A few weeks before I met the prairie chickens, I was fortunate to observe an unusual family of Whooping Cranes on a coastal wetland within the Aransas National Wildlife Refuge. Successful Whooping Crane pairs usually have a single juvenile in tow. This pair had two! The last time a pair brought "twins" to Texas was 1964. In 1941 only 15 cranes were counted at Aransas. This winter there were 183! The Intercoastal Waterway now cuts through the heart of the wetlands vital to the Whooping Cranes. One spill of toxic chemicals could decimate the population.

Those grasslands where the prairie chickens still dance near Texas City were spared through the generosity of private corporations and the excellent work of the Nature Conservancy of Texas and the State of Texas. The wetlands where the Whooping Cranes continue to dance were saved by the federal government. Combining the conservation efforts of private land owners, corporations, nongovernment organizations such as Audubon and The Nature Conservancy and state and federal governments will help assure that wildlife will continue to prosper in Texas to the enrichment of our own species.

INTERNATIONAL CRANE FOUNDATION
George Archibald, Director

The Endangered Species Media Project gratefully acknowledges the support of

United Space Alliance
The Powell Foundation
Rohm & Haas Company
The Houston Endowment
Vastar Resources, Incorporated
Compaq Computer Corporation
A.V. "Army" Emmott, Bookbinders
The Cynthia & George Mitchell Foundation

Many people have helped to make this book possible. It is a pleasure to recognize the assistance of Janice Adamson, Steve Astrich, Robie Brewington (Professor of Anthropology, University of Houston - Clear Lake), Carolyn Farb, Patricia Fox, Michael Herrera, Celia Homer, Michael Hunt (Professor of Psychology, University of Houston - Clear Lake), Selaine Messem, Marilyn Rupley, Christopher Sheridan, Joanie Whitebird and Gary Woods.

For further information about Vanishing Wildlife of Texas, contact:
Endangered Species Media Project
1813 Missouri • Houston, Texas 77006 • 713/520-1985

CONTENTS

Foreword

It is said that "Everything is bigger in Texas." To anyone who has experienced the diverse wonders of the state, from its climate and topography to its cornucopia of cultural and natural resources, this is the humbling truth. Texas is lucky enough to have a lion's share of what our planet has to offer. This places, therefore, a bigger-than-average responsibility on Texans to maintain their incredible human and natural heritage.

At this time as the world has rolled over into a new millennium, we humans are applying the greatest pressure ever on the environment, not only by our extraordinary, ever-increasing numbers but by our sophisticated and uncompromising technical warfare on soils, waterways and the air we breathe. The trouble is, we are not only affecting ourselves, but every animate and inanimate organism around us. A Native American, Chief Seattle, summed it up in this way: "Man did not weave the web of life, man is but a strand in the web. Whatever he does to the web, he does to himself. All things are connected." These are incredibly astute words and apply more than ever in present times.

America is the most privileged country on the planet. Again, this puts Texas very high on the ladder of accountability to recognize, preserve and protect its wonderful, varied state. We are indeed fortunate to have *Vanishing Wildlife of Texas* as a beacon to light the way.

Robert Bateman

Arid mountains etched in ancient colors ascend skyward, while jade and turquoise desert plants flow like icing over towering cliffs. Gentle mists from cascading springs cool the hot summer breeze. Herbs, wildflowers, grapes and mescal plants, once harvested by indigenous people, are still in abundance. Elk and deer traverse the high country, quench their thirst at springs, and graze on bounteous flora. Along the creeks are groves of little walnut, velvet ash, mulberry, mock orange, desert willow and the huge faxon yucca. Higher up, in a relict forest, stands of Douglas fir, ponderosa pine, juniper, and occasional aspen shade ancient Guadalupe mountaintop campgrounds long ago abandoned by the Mescalero tribes.

Few portions of Texas' landscape, such as these mountaintops, have remained unchanged from the way they appeared centuries ago. What must have seemed a measureless expanse to immigrants has been tamed and settled. Texas' diverse ecosystems of deserts, grasslands, forests, rivers, and bayous have been quarried, drilled, slashed, dammed, subdivided, and filled with livestock, oil wells, and factories. The increasingly rare wilderness areas and natural habitats that have not been so altered represent Texas' fleeting natural heritage.

Introduction

In 1528, a storm on Texas coastal waters cast shipwrecked Spanish explorers ashore. These were the first Europeans to set foot on Texas soil. Indigenous people, who annually visited the coastal islands, rescued some of the sailors and nourished them back to health, only to enslave them. One of the castaways, Alvar Nunez Cabeza de Vaca, later wrote about his adventure.

Along the barrier islands lived two nomadic tribes: the Capoques and the Hans, who travelled to coastal islands every fall to harvest a small, walnut-size root from the brackish waters near shore. The bulb was difficult to dig out, and de Vaca was assigned to help women perform the task.

When the roots began to grow, they became bitter and unpalatable, so in February the nomads packed their possessions into canoes and crossed over to the mainland. They camped by a bay for three months, enjoying plentiful oysters until May, then moved to the coastal prairie for blackberries. The area was teaming with wildlife including the river otter, beaver and mink. The reddish egret, brown pelican, least tern and piping plover were common along the coastline. The whooping crane still migrated in healthy numbers, and the manatee populated the

coastal waters along with numerous species of large sea turtles.

As the tribes moved further inland, they gathered and hunted food such as fruit, herbs, roots, cactus, fresh-water fish, deer, bear and buffalo. Cane was used for arrows and sinew for bowstrings and binding. Some bands wore no clothing, using alligator and shark fat to ward off mosquitoes.

De Vaca's captors eventually allowed him to help trade among the Charruco, who inhabited forests along the inland streams and rivers. Pecan groves along the river bottoms were the site of an annual gathering of the tribes. Pecans were ground and stored. Sycamore, elm, green ash, sweet gum and other tree species in that region once harbored birds like the pileated woodpecker, white-breasted nuthatch, Carolina chickadee, chuck-will's-widow, and Kentucky warbler. Other aboriginal species such as the red wolf, black bear and ocelot roamed the region, and wildflowers like South Texas ambrosia and slender rush-pea flourished there.

In 1534 de Vaca was allowed to travel down the coast. At a "river of nuts" (probably the Guadalupe), he found three of his former companions, two of whom had lived with another coastal tribe. From the lower Guadalupe southwest to the Rio Grande, the reunited survivors journeyed through the coastal sand plains and South Texas brush country. Unusual species such as the margay and jaguarundi were indigenous to the region, along with extraordinary birds like the wood stork and tropical parula warbler. All are now in danger of extinction.

The Europeans spent slightly more than two years among the Mariames and Avavares. Through this experience de Vaca later recorded unique ethnographic information. He specifically mentioned the fare of a tribe called the Yguazes, who ate spiders, ant eggs, worms, lizards, snakes, rotten wood and deer dung. One group, probably part of the Coahuilteco tribe, had an appetite for foods more appealing to him, such as cacti, mesquite beans, seeds, nuts and berries.

After crossing the lower Rio Grande, de Vaca and his companions traversed northern Mexico and reentered Texas at the confluence of the Rio Grande and Rio Concho. This part of West Texas was home to magnificent wildlife species such as the gray wolf, black bear and golden eagle. In the Trans-Pecos region, the Europeans encountered a tribe called Jumanos, who lived in permanent dwellings and grew maize, beans and melons along the Rio Grande. Their seasonal migrations to the north to hunt buffalo caused de Vaca to refer to the Jumanos as Cow People.

In the wilderness of the Chihuahuan Desert, cacti, yuccas, sotol, greasewood and other fruits of the desert were gathered. Tender

new leaves of the prickly-pear cactus and mesquite pods were boiled for food, and jelly was made from the cactus fruit. The blossoms of yucca were edible and chunks of the sprouted basal leaves were cut for chewing; the pulp was sweet. The fruit of the strawberry cactus was eaten. A brew from the sunflower was used in case of sunstroke, and century plants were used for soap, medicine and fibers.

Ultimately reaching a Mexican outpost in 1536, de Vaca reported having seen indications of gold. This caused excitement among Spaniards who were anxious to sponsor follow-up expeditions into West Texas. However, upon returning to Spain in 1542, de Vaca belittled the value of most of Texas and its inhabitants.

Shortly after de Vaca's adventure, Hernando de Soto brought hundreds of soldiers under his command to Florida in 1539. He traveled through the Southeast in search of an overland route to Mexico. Upon de Soto's death in 1542, command was released to Luis de Mosocso Alvarado. Entering Texas, Alvarado encountered several of the Caddo tribes along the course of the Red, Angelina, and Neches Rivers. The Caddo maintained permanent settlements for several thousand years prior to European contact. They gathered and processed fruits, nuts and berries and cultivated small fields of maize, several varieties of beans, squash, pumpkins, watermelons and sunflowers. Buffalo, deer and bear were plentiful, and a wide variety of fish filled the pristine rivers and streams.

The Bidai, one of the Caddo speaking tribes, lived in the northern territory they called the "Big Woods," now known as the Big Thicket. The many small streams were clear and cold with bountiful plants such as the bottle gentian, sweet pepper bush and smooth alder growing along the banks. An extraordinary biological diversity provided food and protective cover for hundreds of species. Beaver prospered in ponds, lakes, rivers and streams. Mink favored small streams. River otters searched for fish and crayfish. The black bear and red wolf thrived there. Red-cockaded woodpeckers were also plentiful.

Rolling grasslands flourished in uplands between the streams, with principal species of longleaf pine, bluestem grasses and hundreds of wildflowers like the bird-foot violet, winecup and purple pleat-leaf. Where northern uplands graded down, longleaf pines reached a perimeter realm with beech, magnolia, loblolly pine and rare wildflowers like the Carolina lily and Indian pipe. Some herbs found there, which were used as medicines by the indigenous people and early immigrants, included puccoon, slender gayfeather, Texas Dutchman's-pipe and silkgrass.

Almost simultaneous with de Soto's journey, Francisco Vasquez de Coronado's expedition to the West was the first contact of Europeans with the Plains Indians of Texas. One of the tribes Coronado encountered was the Querechos. The slow migrations of buffalo herds defined the nomadic nature of these people who were probably members of the eastern Apaches. The tribe settled in the spring and summer to till gardens and small fields. In the fall, they packed their possessions onto travois, which were pulled by large dogs, and followed the buffalo to the South Plains.

The High Plains are noted for the absence of any distinct or identifiable features. Coronado navigated this deep sea of grass by magnetic compass. At times his expedition crossed native grasses so high that progress was marked by ordering a foot soldier to count every step taken by Coronado's horse. These great plains, prairies and cross-timber regions were home to unusual creatures like the black-footed ferret, white-faced ibis and Texas horned lizard, as well as brilliantly colored wildflowers like the Texas poppy-mallow and large-fruited sand-verbena.

In the summer of 1541 Coronado encountered people known as the Wichitas. Hunting the buffalo was less essential to them than to other plains people, because they cultivated an abundance of corn, beans and squash. They also thrived on pecans and the fruit of the prickly-pear cactus.

Although Coronado, Alvarado, de Vaca and other Spanish expeditions explored this land we now call Texas, Spain essentially ignored the region for the next 200 years. She could not defend all of her empire from European rivals, but diligently investigated intrusions by other Europeans.

Frenchman Rene Robert Cavelier, Sieur de La Salle, came down the Mississippi River in 1682, claiming its entire basin for his country. Desiring to establish a base near the mouth of the Mississippi, La Salle returned to the Gulf of Mexico in 1685.

Missing his intended destination, La Salle sailed instead to the Texas coastal waters known today as Matagorda Bay. A landing party went ashore and found mud flats, oyster beds, and no fresh water. Some of the men were captured by a local tribe, forcing La Salle to enter their village with a rescue party. The tribe soon made amends by releasing the captives and bringing peace offerings of buffalo and dolphin meat.

Adjusting to the new environs was difficult for the colonists. Within a few days one man was dead from snakebite, one was

hanged, and several deserters were lost in the wilderness. In the spring, gardens were planted to provide fresh food, but by mid summer wild animals and drought had almost totally destroyed the crops.

La Salle's men completed construction of Fort St. Louis in November of 1685. He then set out to explore land as far as the Rio Grande. One of his men returned to the colony reporting that six men had been killed by natives, their bodies torn to pieces by wolves. La Salle and his depleted expedition returned to the settlement at the end of March, bringing dried buffalo meat. Stocks of ammunition were low, and the colonists were barely able to defend themselves against hostile tribes. Worse still, the colony's only remaining ship, *Belle*, had run aground and broken up.

La Salle took a small party northeast looking for the Mississippi River. One man was eaten by an alligator, four more deserted and seven were lost in the wilderness. The French leader was eventually killed by his own men near the Navasota River. Natives later attacked the tiny fort, killing all of the adults.

In 1686, Captain Alonzo de Leon of Spain entered Texas by land from south of the Rio Grande to search for any foreign intruders. De Leon commented favorably on the lush greenery of this portion of the province, while observing that the fields of the natives contained bounteous crops of corn, beans, squash, watermelons and cantaloupes. He was amazed at the abundance of bison and vast numbers of other unusual species.

Finding the ruins of La Salle's compound, he had the remnants of the site burned. Mission San Francisco de los Tejas was established, but that tiny wooden compound just southwest of present-day Nacogdoches was abandoned in 1693.

In 1714, the French established a trading post on the Red River at Natchitoches. They considered Texas theirs because of La Salle's earlier occupation. Highly prized pelts of beaver, mink, jaguar, cougar, bobcat, raccoon, wolf and bison were coveted by the Europeans. This valuable merchandise delighted the continental elite and was exported en masse. Many of these wildlife species have never recovered from this intensive early fur trapping.

French commander Jean Baptiste Benard de La Harpe sailed for Texas and established a trading post near modern Texarkana in 1719. Upon entering the Trinity River area he noted the fine prairie and forests along the river's high banks. The native people entertained him in their camp, offering grain, roots and smoked meat. His party was especially welcome to the Wichitas, who had begun receiving firearms supplied by La Harpe and other Frenchmen.

By 1730, the French were trading on a larger scale with tribes like the Orcoquiza on the lower Trinity and San Jacinto Rivers for bear, deer and buffalo skins. The newly-acquired guns accelerated the slaughter, and the decline of many species was inevitable. The indigenous people realized that their hunting skills and knowledge of the native fauna could provide furs and skins sought by Europeans. It was to their advantage to use these commodities as barter.

European squatters and roving frontiersman were common in East Texas and were also present in small numbers at the Alamo, which had been built in 1718 by Spanish missionaries. The Spanish governor unofficially became the head trader serving southeastern Texas. He began quietly buying goods from his French enemies in Natchitoches or New Orleans and used his troops to deliver the contraband merchandise to Indian villages on the San Jacinto and Trinity Rivers in exchange for large quantities of furs and hides.

By the late 1700's, aggressive American expansionists were exploring Texas. Planters had their eyes on the region, but most of the new inhabitants of Texas were still squatters and trappers who continued to profit from their uncontrolled exploitation of wildlife. The purchase of Louisiana by the United States in 1803 transformed Nacogdoches into one of the most strategic cities in Spain's empire. The town served as the first barrier against the spread of the United States.

European and Anglo-American merchants interested in the Indian trade financed volunteers willing to go to Texas in 1819. Other foreign entrepreneurs were now welcome to develop the Texas frontier, taking advantage of new policies established in the declining days of the Spanish empire.

In 1820, Moses Austin received an empresario contract from the Spanish government, but he died before coming to Texas. His son, Stephen F. Austin, brought 300 families to Texas to plant cotton, just as Mexico was winning independence from Spain.

There were cattle ranchers in East Texas who brought families and animals by land from southwestern Louisiana. People from the Mississippi Valley were homesteading in Texas as settlements materialized in 1822.

Texas was supplying New Orleans with even larger exports of animal skins and bear grease traded by the Cushattas on the Trinity River. Corn, butter and cotton were also shipped out on small schooners and sloops from Galveston.

Two overland routes brought streams of Americans to Texas. An ancient trail, the San Antonio Road or "Camino Real," developed into a European trade route and stretched from Louisiana through Natchitoches to San Antonio, while the old Opelousas-Atascosita Road ran from Opelousas, Louisiana, to Laredo, Texas. Other colonists came by sea, porting at the mouth of the Brazos River, then moving inland to their homesteads. Financiers petitioned the Mexican government for empresario contracts. These included German merchants who settled hundreds of families in 1826 and again in 1828.

Texas' unspoiled land and seemingly limitless game and fish populations from the woodland territories to the rolling prairies became world renowned. Adding to the land rush, word got out that crops like corn and cotton grew without much work. Prairies never before grazed by livestock provided unimaginably fertile pastures. Massive forests supplied abundant building materials. From swamps and bayous to crystal-clear streams and untamed rivers, the Texas wilderness appeared to be a virtually unlimited, unchecked, unregulated, unrestricted and untapped wealth of nature.

People from far and wide poured into Texas in the 1820s. Farmers and ranchers sent crops and cattle to New Orleans, along with larger exports of bear grease, game and tens of thousands of furs and hides.

Texas landscapes were being exploited, cleared, plowed and parceled, with little or no concern for conservation. If one homestead played out, it was easy to pull up stakes and move to another piece of land. Cotton, corn and cattle changed the native habitat as wild creatures were driven out, and signs of erosion and silting of waterways began. Denuded forests and prairies turned to dust and mud, then blew away or washed into streams and waterways. Farmers and ranchers disrupted the native flora and fauna on a massive scale.

Slaves and equipment were being brought to Texas to plant and process cotton crops and raise livestock on an even larger scale. Plantation owners and ranchers increased exports of goods being shipped on schooners. Merchants sent farm products to New Orleans or to Mexican ports in exchange for materials and staple goods to expand plantations. Large sailing ships brought Texans commodities such as flour and tobacco.

Steamboats arrived in Texas in the 1830s. Early timber operations used them to haul lumber and firewood to the Gulf after floating the logs downriver. Oxen provided a method of transporting logs to the rivers. Two-wheeled ox-carts with huge wheels measuring up to five feet high moved logs, easily rolling over fallen trees and huge stumps. Rushing rivers then swept the logs downstream to sawmills.

The potential magnitude of the lumber industry had been quickly recognized. Austin predicted that timber operations would be very extensive through all of East Texas within a few years. Sawmills were already operating on Buffalo Bayou and the San Jacinto River.

Loggers were originally drawn to Texas by the tremendous stands of longleaf and loblolly pines. In later years, lumbermen also found profit in the hardwood forests, cutting the stately beech and cypress that once lined the waterways of the Big Thicket. Towns had sprung up throughout the region during the 1830's; however, the major assault on the Texas wilderness was yet to come.

Near Navasota, at Washington-on-the-Brazos, Texas independence was declared on March 2, 1836. Texas became a nation in April of that year. Mexican soldiers were quickly put to work planting crops and rebuilding homes that had been destroyed by their army. Others labored cutting wood for the steamboats.

New private-venture towns were founded because of strategic locations to steamboat landings. As more furs and crops were exported, more merchandise could be imported. Ships came loaded with passengers and departed laden with cotton bales. Slaves produced corn and cotton for the Galveston market; lowland plantations experimented with crops of sugar cane.

In 1838, riverboat companies regularly scheduled trips to Houston from Galveston Island, while larger steamboats operated between Galveston Island and New Orleans. By 1845, nearly twenty-five thousand acres of cotton were being grown, mostly along the Brazos and Colorado Rivers and in East Texas. Corn and sugar

cane were important cash crops, and ranching became successful. Schooners and sloops filled ports as towns continued to expand to meet the needs of exporters and burgeoning populations.

After Texas was annexed by the United States, shipping interests saw a chance for the federal government to provide dredging operations for the ports. Lumber companies established complete sawmill towns with thousands of employees. Steam powered sawmills were operating in strategic locations along major rivers.

Many homesteaders moved from the coast to prime upland farms and ranches. Land was so cheap that farmers were apathetic about soil conservation on their acreage. When the soil was depleted, it was easy to move to new sites. Deserted lowland plantations were common. Still, the overall coastal population was rapidly increasing. Every person that went inland was replaced by three new residents. Farmland, and the corn harvest, more than quadrupled in Houston county in the 1850's, while cotton production increased almost ten times.

Farmers lacked proper understanding of crop rotation and conservation; farm and plantation soils played out. Ranchers grazed too much livestock in the uplands. Topsoils were exposed and washed away, causing floods. In the bottomlands of the Brazos and Colorado Rivers native grasses also vanished to overgrazing, along with the extensive canebrakes and other vegetation. Once clear running streams became muddied from eroded soils.

On South Texas ranges, heavy brush plants invaded pastures, replacing grasses that livestock had ravaged. Horsemen were unable to ride through thorns and thickets, which began filling previously open grasslands between Corpus Christi and the Rio Grande.

People went farther west. One southern route along the road from San Antonio to El Paso had moved thousands of immigrants in 1849. The following year marked the beginning of the American epoch. In 1850, vast areas were opened by the state to pioneer residents. Railroads received huge grants, immense areas were sold, and settlement by ranchers was encouraged. But no lands were set aside to preserve wilderness and wildlife.

Ranchers poured all the livestock they could acquire onto the range, causing a great reduction in wildlife species and practically obliterated flowering plants. Native flora must bloom in order to reproduce and does not survive rigorous grazing. Delicate grasses had originally provided sod, with pools of rainwater holding moisture for months. These grasslands were converted into eroded desert.

Overgrazing left acre upon acre with bare, sun-baked sand and gravel. Nothing remained in this man-made desert but creosote, Spanish dagger and tarbush. It will take eons to bring grasses back, and the land may never be able to rebuild. Huge cattle populations ate the prime grass. Sheep and goats were then brought in to forage on what remained, tearing out the roots and pounding the earth to dust. Thus we see the truth in John Muir's dictum, "as sheep advance, flowers, vegetation, grass, soil, plenty and poetry vanish."

Livestock had taken over the West. Ranchers claimed more and more rangeland that supported fewer and fewer cattle per acre. Twenty-five acres of land were required to graze an animal that originally needed only two to five acres.

In 1878, barbed wire came from Illinois. It could have served a conservation potential by allowing rotation of livestock on grazing land, but ranchers continued over-stocking their acreage. By 1884, many who had speculated heavily in livestock went bankrupt — their animals died of starvation on the denuded and ruined ranges.

Destruction of predators also led to disastrous imbalances. Ranchers who destroyed wolves and big cats to protect their cattle caused huge increases in the coyote population. In later years, when they set out to eradicate coyotes, the rodent population soared out of control. There is no simple way to determine what will occur when the predator-prey balance of nature is altered by mass destruction of any one species. People were more concerned with subduing the wild than with understanding the real effects of their actions.

In East Texas piney woods, entrepreneurs purchased mammoth timber acreage at rock-bottom prices from homesteaders who saw a chance to have their land cleared and make a little money. Before settlers realized the potential profit of their woodland properties, they often sold the timber rights as cheaply as fifty cents per acre. Texas was steadily rising in the ranks of timber-producing states in the 1880's.

Cutting practices of early loggers contributed to the rapid destruction of the Big Woods. Its timber supplies were thought to be inexhaustible, so pioneer timber companies felt no obligation to reforest their land. The first assault by timber magnates was against the longleaf pine. This tree was the monarch of the Southeast Texas forests, reaching over 120 feet high and living hundreds of years. Its wood was prized for its great strength.

Ancient upland longleaf pine forests originally had a thick "closed canopy" that heavily shaded the forest floor, allowing delicate shade-tolerant flora to evolve in areas of less undergrowth. Destruction of these "cathedral forests" led to the invasion of tangled thickets and heavy undergrowth, drastically altering the ecosystem.

Longleaf pine and mixed pine-hardwood forests provided excellent habitat for the red wolf, black bear, wood stork, red-cockaded woodpecker, ivory-billed woodpecker, and many other birds and mammals that are now endangered. The vanishing alligator snapping turtle, paddlefish, bluehead shiner minnow, blackside darter, American burying beetle and numerous other threatened species once thrived in woodland streams and underbrush. Delicate plants such as the Texas trailing phlox and Navasota ladies'-tresses orchid grew in the shade of the forest canopy and thus have almost completely disappeared.

Hunting continued to annihilate vast populations of Texas species. When species were over hunted and became scarce in one area, campsites were moved and hunting began again. With improvements in firearms, the large-scale slaughter of wild animals led to increasing urban markets, further jeopardizing many species' existence.

Export of bird plumage for adornment on women's hats in Europe and in the eastern U.S. led to the decimation of great numbers of coastal bird species. According to Robin Doughty in *Wildlife and Man in Texas*, demand was so high that commercial hunters supplied tens of thousands of great egrets to traders. Vast flocks of water birds nested or wintered on the coast. A single gunman could shoot thousands of birds each week, with the huge kills going to dealers willing to pay up to forty cents apiece for herons and twenty cents for terns.

Hunters killed enormous numbers of herons, gulls, egrets, skimmers, cranes, curlews, plovers and other shorebirds. Brilliantly colored songbirds went to market as well.

Legislators tended to shy away from measures controlling individual privileges, so the first laws for hunting control had little practical impact. They did recognize that wild animals had become limited. Unfortunately, the Civil War forced wildlife conservation to a low priority, effectively ending regulations for the remainder of the nineteenth century.

In the decades after the Civil War, shippers began to send huge quantities of game birds from distant ports by rail. The grouse, turkey, quail and other upland game birds dis-

appeared from many areas. Railroads and the development of refrigeration opened up the state for people who had supplied local markets in Galveston, Houston and San Antonio with cheap game meat. St. Louis, Chicago and other northern cities became outlets for Texas game; dealers sold hundreds of thousands of game birds annually. In New York, for example, a federal official recorded a single consignment of 20,000 prairie chickens — totaling twenty tons.

Marketers also took advantage of the region's abundant seafood. Commercial fishermen quickly depleted stocks from lakes, rivers and coastal waters. Seine nets contributed to overfishing. Explosives were even tossed into the water to kill large quantities of aquatic life.

Texas shores were also nesting grounds for five species of marine turtles. The green turtle was netted in coastal waters and shipped live to New Orleans and East Coast markets where it was prized for its meat. Other turtles were processed into meat and soup in Texas canneries. Many thousands of the now endangered sea turtles ended up as turtle soup.

Public officials and citizens realized that numerous species of wildlife were declining because of exploitation, but most authorities failed to voice their opinions. With vast populations of birds migrating from northern territories, it was taken for granted that such wildlife fecundity was inexhaustible. The passenger pigeons, for example, flocked to the south in unimaginable numbers. Hunters could kill them by the score with one blast from a double-barreled shotgun. By the turn of the century the species was gone. In the last few decades of the nineteenth century, the bison and antelope were also extirpated from Texas, and hunters finished off the remaining strongholds of other wildlife for meat and sport.

Fragmented natural habitats could not support healthy populations of wildlife as settlers cleared millions of acres of land for cotton and corn in the late 1800s. With little crop rotation or concern for soil conservation, depletion and erosion through continuous monocropping had far reaching effects on wildlife habitats.

The ineffectual and powerless state conservation agencies seemed apathetic and neglected official duty. At the turn of the century, legislators' insufficient attempts to place closed seasons on specific game species such as the pronghorn antelope and bighorn sheep were not enforceable. During and immediately after World War I, wildlife populations dropped even more dramatically.

After 1920, the state made some meager efforts to capture and transfer game animals to areas where they had vanished, but wildlife agencies concluded the bleak outlook had never been worse. The conservation movement fluctuated in Texas. Studies by the Audubon Society of remote islands where wildlife and nesting places existed for rare species became more publicized.

Texas lawmakers, in 1921, authorized the General Land Office to lease Big Bird Island, Little Bird Island and Green Island to the National Audubon Society, without charge, rendering these critical habitats completely protected. A 1925 law afforded a plan for private game preserves. Through its provisions some landowners agreed to foster game placement and to protect species of game animals for not less than ten years. Reintroduction increased numbers of some game species on private lands. In the first year, thirty-three game preserves totaling more than one million acres were initiated.

During the Great Depression of the 1930's, Texans perceived the barren deficiencies resulting from wildlife having been wiped out of vast areas. Preservation approaches garnered initiative as the state worked with landowners to increase private reserves to fifty-three, encompassing 2.7 million acres.

The Aransas National Wildlife Refuge, the first federal refuge in Texas, was established in 1937 to conserve waterfowl. It included a small flock of approximately fourteen whooping cranes wintering in the tidal marshes of the Blackjack Peninsula in Aransas County.

Management plans were being drawn up by conservation agencies to complement hunting regulations with a perspective on restocking animals. Bison, antelope, bighorn sheep, prairie chickens, turkey and quail were being evaluated for reintroduction to their native range.

After World War II, however, farming expansion and urban growth put most fallow lands to more extensive use. Areas that had been potential sites for reintroduction were highly confined by the proportion and magnitude of habitat disintegration from the growth of urban areas and agriculture landscapes. Many of the remaining potential reintroduction territories had developed into the state's principal agri-business regions for the growing of cotton and grain.

Cities and metropolitan areas rapidly swelled in population throughout Texas. Designs to bring back categories of native game species that could be acclimated to such environmental transformations were restricted. Basically, there were no places left to restore wildlife. In the 1950s, Texas did make some

progress toward establishing public systems of refuges, but in the following decades, lagged behind other states in its program of land acquisition.

To date, Texas has fifty state wildlife management areas, eight state fish hatcheries, thirteen national wildlife refuges, four national forests, five national grasslands and 126 state parks, historic sites and natural areas. The idea of preserving biodiversity as a natural heritage for future generations has become popular in recent decades. However, each year we still lose thousands of acres of our wilderness legacy. Despite some success stories, most endangered resource programs are underfunded and understaffed.

Texas consists of 267,000 square miles, nearly 800 miles wide and almost 800 miles long, with 80,000 miles of rivers and streams, 190 man-made lakes and reservoirs and one natural lake (Caddo Lake). A number of mammal, bird, reptile, amphibian and fish species are Texas originals, found only in our state. Twenty-one vertebrate species have completely disappeared from Texas. Thirty-one species of mammals, twenty species of birds, twenty-seven species of reptiles, twelve amphibian species, twenty species of fish, five species of invertebrates and twenty-two species of plants are listed as threatened or endangered by the Texas Parks and Wildlife Department.

Because of its biotic complexity, Texas is a unique state with ten distinct vegetative zones, from the Piney Woods of East Texas to the Trans-Pecos, and from the Lower Rio Grande Valley to the Llano Estacado. The current human population of more than 17 million shares habitat and terrain with nearly 600 species of birds, 142 species of mammals, and more than 100 species of snakes. The Lone Star State was, and still is, a rich and complex region. But what seemed to be endless wilderness, woodlands and natural resources not so long ago has given way to urbanization, deforestation, destruction of wetlands, cropland expansion and agricultural intensification.

Habitat change remains the most challenging issue for conservationists and the greatest threat to wildlife. The question remains whether growing numbers of rare or threatened flora and fauna will disappear from the state or whether efforts to save endangered species will be successful.

The disappearance of various species can set off chain reactions that cause the loss of other native species. What is the long-term impact? The value of what is lost may be too complex to be completely comprehended. Wildlife diversity is equal to habitat diversity. It does not matter what we do to restore wildlife populations if there is no habitat left to support them.

Not long ago, Texas was carpeted with virgin forests, great plains grasses and delicate wetland and desert flora. Today the minute residue of that heritage faces daily encroachment by development. Habitat has been destroyed by activities such as channelization, draining, and leveeing of rivers and bayous; disposal of the materials from dredging of channels and marinas; and draining and filling of wetlands. Loss or alteration of wetlands habitat destroys areas where many species live or breed.

Numerous creeks in certain parts of the Balcones Escarpment that historically were recharged by permanent springs from subterranean aquifers now are dry because of groundwater pumping and agricultural practices. Free-flowing creeks of the eastern parts of Texas have diminished for many of the same reasons. Foremost of these are pumping, damming, timber clearing and overgrazing by livestock of watershed habitats.

Farming chemicals have also altered and continue to affect ecosystems. Their use can result in loss of ability for soil to absorb and retain moisture. Water runs off, rather than seeping in, and carries topsoil with it, decreasing productivity of the land. This leads to a vicious cycle of more chemical fertilizer. Eventually, unreplenished aquifers can affect the carrying capacity of the land.

Pesticides are slowly rendering our groundwater undrinkable and threatening our wildlife. In the last half century, hundreds of insect species have developed resistance to chemical pesticides. Over the past two decades, weeds have also become resistant to the chemical herbicides that are polluting our environment and our food.

Residue from agricultural chemicals has been detected in groundwater, lakes and streams as a result of runoff from treated fields. Many of these chemicals are persistent in soil and water, with residues found in wildlife — from birds and their eggs to free-living fish. Farm and lawn fertilizers, pesticides and herbicides, hazardous chemicals, oil and other toxins stored in landfills or leaking from storage tanks, and transportation spills are poisoning our lakes, streams and waterways.

Seagrasses and submersed vascular plants, which provide food and habitat to diverse animal populations, have declined and died back in many aquatic systems due to runoff of farming chemicals and herbicides.

Chemical fertilizers seep into waterways, creating algae blooms. Organisms that decompose the abundance of algae then consume all the available oxygen, leaving patches of water that have been almost totally depleted of oxygen. These are a probable cause of huge "dead zones" hundreds of miles long adrift in the Gulf of Mexico. Marine life cannot survive without oxygenated water.

The cumulative impact of all these activities has destroyed critical habitats and resulted in deterioration of important resources. Contamination of fish and sediment risks public health and wildlife, as well as mounting threats to the entire region and economy. Fishing advisories warn women of childbearing age and children against consuming certain fish in various locations.

Aquatic life is also contaminated by pathogens such as disease-causing bacteria and viruses. Incidence of illness (including gastroenteritis, hepatitis A and cholera) from eating contaminated fish is rising. In addition, shellfish beds are often closed because of pollution, resulting in millions of dollars in lost revenues. Many of us have experienced the results of these problems firsthand, such as beach closings caused by contaminated waters, garbage and even medical wastes.

Even though treatment of sewage and industrial waste has improved considerably in the past decade, they still account for a substantial portion of water pollutants. Heavy metals and thousands of recently invented chemicals, which normal treatment does not remove and which are not broken down by nature, are non-biodegradable. Other hazards, such as leachate from hazardous waste storage sites and landfills and deposition of pollutants from the air, have very tangible monetary costs. Airborne toxins eventually poison our land and water, killing fish and wildlife and endangering humans.

Chlorofluorocarbons (CFCs) used in refrigerators, air conditioners and cleaning agents deplete the ozone layer, a protective shield that screens out harmful ultraviolet radiation from the sun. Regulations on these man-made time bombs are now coming into effect, but whether they are strong enough — or soon enough — to avoid problems with our global ecosystem, only time will tell.

Recently, human activities have also turned up the global thermostat through the release of unprecedented amounts of carbon

dioxide, methane and nitrous oxide into the atmosphere. These gases permit the sun's heat to penetrate, but block heat from escaping by absorbing the longer-wavelength infrared radiation. Some scientists think that if we do not reduce these "greenhouse gasses" our planet could reach a point where many species, including humans, are in crisis.

In an incredibly short time, human beings have caused an extremely accelerated rate of extinction. This destruction stems in large part from the prevailing philosophy, "us against nature." We behave as if wilderness and nature are nothing more than impediments to be overcome. Today, more than ever, we must see the error in this approach to dealing with our environment.

Each time we break one link in the web of life, every other form of life is disrupted and endangered as a consequence. What we tend to forget is that *all* living things are interconnected and interdependent, and that the destruction of any one component of the web of nature can have profound implications for all the rest. We are a dependent part of nature, not removed from it. Wilderness is essential for the survival of all species, including us. As Henry David Thoreau so aptly stated, "In wildness is the preservation of the world."

Endangered Species Media Project
Frank Salzhandler

© GAMINI RATNAVIRA

OCELOT

Felis pardalis

JAGUARUNDI

Felis yagouaroundi

The last faint glow of the setting sun has faded in the western sky, and the insistent song of a pauraque fills the night. From atop a twisted, gnarled mesquite snag comes the booming call of a great horned owl. Then a wraithlike shadow crosses a patch of moonlit grass, disappearing into a thicket of coastal scrub. Sleek and lithe, the animal moves with deliberate grace, revealing for one short moment a pattern of dark spots on its back and flanks. Its long tail is ringed with black.

Just as quickly the cat is gone, lost in the thorny, impenetrable tangle of black-brush and prickly-pear. Like a ghost in the night it vanishes, but the fleeting glimpse will be etched forever in the mind. For this is an ocelot, a rare and endangered animal that has often been called the most beautiful of the world's wild cats. Only a few still roam the dense thorn-scrub woodlands north of the Rio Grande.

Ocelots, *Felis pardalis*, once ranged across the southern portions of the state and northward along the coastal plain to the Big Thicket of East Texas. Others inhabited the Edwards Plateau, where they found homes in caves along the rocky bluffs and in hollow trees. Regrettably, those days are gone forever, and the ocelot now occurs only in isolated patches of remnant brushlands across three or four counties of the lower Rio Grande Valley.

Estimates from surveys conducted in 1993 place the number remaining in Texas at between eighty and 120 individuals; thirty to thirty-five of those live in or near Laguna Atascosa National Wildlife Refuge. Fully protected by Texas law, the ocelot was also placed on the federal list of endangered species on March 30, 1972. Although this beautiful cat occurs sparingly southward through Central and South America, it is endangered throughout its range.

About the size of the more common and familiar bobcat, but with a long tail, the ocelot is grayish or buffy and heavily marked with a cryptic pattern of dark spots, rings and bars. Whitish underparts are also spotted with black.

Ocelots become active at dark and hunt through the night, feeding on a variety of small mammals including rabbits, wood rats and mice. Birds, snakes, lizards, various amphibians and occasional fish supplement their diet. Sunrise finds them bedded down for the day, sometimes in a different spot each morning. Females may roam a territory of up to two square miles; the more restless males can roam twice that much.

Before giving birth to her litter of one or two kittens, the female prepares a den that is often little more than a shallow depression scraped clean of leaf litter. Well hidden in thick brush or dense bunchgrass, however, it is invariably surrounded by a protective wall of thorny shrubs.

Births have been recorded from late spring into December, but most occur between September and November. The mother hunts for food at night and spends the daylight hours at her den, caring for the kittens that are born sparsely furred and with eyes tightly shut. They will begin accompanying her on hunting trips at about three months of age but will remain dependent throughout their first year of life.

The ocelot is one of four endangered wild cats that have ranged northward into Texas from Mexico and tropical America. Two, the small, spotted margay and the much larger jaguar, have not been reported for several years. The fourth, the jaguarundi, is even rarer and more secretive than the ocelot. It was placed on the federal endangered-species list on June 14, 1976.

Somewhat larger than an ordinary house cat, the jaguarundi, *Felis yagouaroundi*, has a slender body, very short legs and a long tail. Its small, unusually flattened head gives it a strangely weasel-like appearance. Two different color phases occur. The grayish form is a grizzled charcoal gray with lighter underparts. It may appear more blackish in winter pelage. A reddish phase has rusty hair mixed with black; its head and legs are brown.

The jaguarundi shares the few remaining brushlands in Cameron, Hidalgo, Starr and Willacy Counties with the ocelot. It, too, hunts primarily at night but is less nocturnal than the ocelot. It may even go to water for a drink during the midday heat. Although the jaguarundi spends most of its time on the ground, it is an expert climber, and birds make up a major portion of a diet that also includes small mammals and reptiles. Little is known about the breeding habits of the jaguarundi, and the size of the Texas population remains the subject of speculation.

Although these rare cats have occasionally been poisoned or shot, habitat loss is the major reason for their decline. Both depend on large tracts of thorn-scrub forest containing such small trees and shrubs as brasil, lotebush, blackbrush, cenizo and guayacan. Less than five percent of the original native vegetation remains along the Mexican border. The remainder has been cleared for citrus, vegetables and sugar cane, or fallen to sprawling urban development.

Studies indicate that at least 100 acres of dense brush is necessary to support ocelots or jaguarundis. Even if they were to survive and reproduce on smaller tracts, there would be nowhere for the young to disperse when forced out by territorial adults.

Personnel from the Caesar Kleberg Research Foundation in Kingsville, Texas, are continuing their studies on the biology of the ocelot and jaguarundi, while the Texas Parks and Wildlife Department and The Nature Conservancy of Texas work with local landowners in an attempt to save or restore critical habitat. The hope is to eventually create corridors of brushland linking the few remaining blocks of riparian forest along the Rio Grande. This offers the only chance for survival not only for the endangered cats but for such rare creatures as the coatimundi, gray hawk and red-billed pigeon, all of which have almost vanished from Texas soil.

Black Bear

Ursus americanus

Black bears once ranged widely throughout the state, inhabiting the mountain ranges of far West Texas, the rugged limestone ledges and outcrops of the Hill Country, and the East Texas bottomland forests. By the early part of this century, however, bears had disappeared from almost all of their former range. They are now fully protected by Texas law, and were placed on the state list of endangered species in 1987. The Louisiana black bear, the form that once inhabited the eastern portions of the state, was also designated a federally threatened species by the U.S. Fish and Wildlife Service in 1992.

This extermination of the black bear in Texas can be attributed largely to hunting. The meat was highly prized by early settlers, and the grease was useful for a number of applications, staying "sweet" almost indefinitely. Some bears were killed solely for sport; others, to protect valuable livestock. East Texas residents, says mammalogist David Schmidly, would not tolerate bears because of their depredations on free-ranging hogs.

Robin Doughty, in *Wildlife and Man in Texas*, tells of a man who crawled into a cave west of New Braunfels and killed five bears, one after the other. He emerged to the wild cheers of the waiting crowd. Other bear hunters in East Texas called their profession both "the hardest work a man ever did" and "the greatest sport on earth."

By 1910, Doughty notes, bears were gone from the Big Thicket except for occasional strays. One shot near Silsbee in 1973 probably wandered across the border from a Louisiana preserve, where a number of black bears trapped in Minnesota had been released as part of a restocking program.

Extensive predator control during the 1930s and 1940s also killed most of the bears and other large predators in the Trans-Pecos region. Big Bend became a national park in 1944, but by that time the black bear was already gone. The same thing has happened in many other portions of the country where bears come in close contact with people. "Only in places that have low human population or an enlightened public," wrote Davis and Schmidly in *The Mammals of Texas*, "have black bears been able to cope successfully with humans."

In spite of its fearsome reputation, the black bear is ordinarily shy and retiring. Surprisingly fleet of foot, it would much rather flee than fight. Black bears are also excellent climbers and often seek refuge in trees, especially when they are young. Adults normally range from about 220 to slightly more than 300 pounds, but some may reach a bulky 500 pounds, according to Davis and Schmidly.

When it comes to food, the black bear is truly omnivorous. It will eat berries and fruit, acorns and pine nuts, a variety of roots and tubers, clover, grass, carpenter ants and other insects, the contents of bee hives and almost any convenient carrion. As campers across the continent have discovered, it also raids knapsacks and garbage cans. Only occasionally does a black bear bring down young deer or livestock, but it is that trait that has spelled trouble for the species.

Black bears do not really hibernate. During cold weather they seek refuge in a windfall or under sheltering ledges and enter a deep sleep; however, their temperature, heartbeat and respiration do not drop dramatically. On warm days they may awaken and wander in search of food, returning to sleep again when the temperature drops.

Most females give birth to twins, but litters can range from one to four. They are normally born in January or February, when the mother is sleeping. Covered with sparse hair and totally blind, the helpless cubs are only six inches long and weigh about a pound. They grow slowly at first, and their eyes do not open for nearly six weeks. By spring, however, they are able to follow their mother on her rounds. They remain with her until the fall of their second year, when she begins to prepare for her next litter.

Bears had been extremely rare in Texas for several decades, but in about 1988, sightings suddenly became more frequent in the Trans-Pecos and even along the fringes of the Edwards Plateau. Most reports came from the Chisos Mountains in Big Bend National Park, and estimates placed the population there at from twelve to twenty bears. Indeed, the discovery of a resident breeding female was the first such report in fifty years.

All of these animals are black bears, it should be noted. There has been only one confirmed specimen of the larger grizzly bear in Texas, an old male killed in the Davis Mountains in 1890. The newcomers to Big Bend and neighboring West Texas belong to a Mexican subspecies of the American black bear and have undoubtedly wandered in from across the Rio Grande. Officials cite two possible reasons for the sudden influx: Mexico banned bear hunting in 1986, and several good breeding seasons had significantly increased populations and pushed the animals northward.

While most Texans delight in the return of black bears to our state, their presence is not without complications. Park officials, biologists and ranchers have competing concerns, and not all look in favor on an increased population of potential predators. One female with two cubs apparently killed a sheep and fifteen Angora goats, and while the bears were successfully captured and moved, the owners demanded compensation. At least two other bears have been shot illegally, and such acts could lead to heavy fines and even prison time for violating the Endangered Species Act.

Public education must be one of the major concerns in managing these new Texas residents. Efforts to control bears outside Big Bend National Park may condemn them all, for the limited habitat within the park is not enough to sustain a population over a long period of time.

For now, black bears once again roam Trans-Pecos Texas, and the possibility exists that they could also reenter the northeastern portions of the state. Restoration efforts in Louisiana and Arkansas are meeting with some success, and an Arkansas population of between 2,000 and 3,000 bears is slowly expanding toward the Texas border.

Neotropical Migrants

The hot, humid afternoon is drawing to a close in a river-bottom forest in deep East Texas, as slanting rays of the setting sun dapple the forest floor. Only the harsh, grating songs of the cicadas and the occasional chatter of a squirrel break the silence. Then from somewhere in the shadows comes a melody of flutelike notes, *ee-o-lay ee-o-lay*, bar after bar of magical music, each phrase rich with overtones and ending in a complex trill. It is the enchanting refrain of the wood thrush *(Hylocichla mustelina)*—vespers for a midsummer day.

Slowly the thrush emerges from a thicket, pausing to look cautiously around. Illuminated by a beam of sunlight, it glows a rich reddish brown, with the brightest hues on the head and neck. White underparts are clearly marked with large, round spots and streaked cheek patches and bold white eye-rings ornament the distinctive face. Throwing back its head, the handsome bird sings once more, then fades again into the shadows.

The wood thrush inhabits wooded swamps and moist forests throughout the eastern half of the United States, from the Canadian border to the Gulf of Mexico.

That breeding range includes East Texas and extends westward to Dallas and Houston. The female lays her three or four blue-green eggs in a bulky cup of leaves, mud, grasses and rootlets and incubates them alone. Both parents, however, feed the young that hatch in about two weeks and fledge twelve or thirteen days later. Insects and other invertebrates constitute the diet of the young, but fruits and berries are added as they grow, making up as much as one-third of the thrush's adult fare.

The wood thrush is one of the gems of the eastern woodlands, but unfortunately it is declining over a substantial portion of its range. It is typical of a large and diverse array of birds called "Neotropical migrants," species that nest in North America and fly long migration routes to spend the winter in Latin America and the Caribbean Islands. There are more than 200 of these long-distance commuters, and their numbers contain many of our most colorful songbirds.

Neotropical migrants include tiny hummingbirds and large hawks, whip-poor-wills and cuckoos. Most of our flycatchers, thrushes, vireos, orioles, grosbeaks, buntings and tanagers move southward to Central and South America for the winter months, for they feed primarily on insects and fruits that are no longer available when chill winds sweep down across the continent.

Most striking of all, perhaps, are the New World warblers, whose names hint at rainbow hues. They include black-throated blue and black-throated green warblers; golden-winged and blue-winged warblers; chestnut-sided, bay-breasted and cerulean warblers. The prothonotary warbler wears golden yellow; the blackburnian is flaming orange. All depart our shores in autumn and return again in spring, sometimes flying nonstop across the Gulf of Mexico.

Many of our Neotropical migrants seem to be declining, and the problems are not always easy to assess. Deforestation across the United States plays an obvious role, as does the loss of native prairie. Indeed, one familiar grassland species, the bobolink, has declined a catastrophic 90 percent throughout the Midwest in recent years.

Statistics obtained from surveys of breeding birds indicate that the colorful painted bunting, arguably one of the South's most beautiful birds, has declined by 58 percent in less than thirty years. "People think its scrubby habitat is wasteland," said one researcher, "so it's being turned into pine plantations or cleared for beach-side condominiums."

Fragmentation of large forest tracts can affect breeding success, even if the total loss of acreage is small. Such fragmentation opens corridors for predators and parasitic cowbirds that normally patrol the woodland edges, bringing them in contact with birds that have as yet developed no defense.

The breeding habits and requirements of most Neotropical migrants have been studied extensively, but we know much less about the remainder of their lives. Habitat loss in tropical America is equally important, whether in the rainforests of Amazonia, the montane woodlands of Venezuela or the pampas of Argentina. Cape May warblers that nest in the United States must find insects in the West Indies; Baltimore and orchard orioles may depend on flowering trees in Guatemala.

Tropical forests are being cut for timber and cleared for banana plantations and cattle ranches. Coffee growers are rapidly converting their shade-grown coffee to more densely planted sun plantations in efforts to increase the yield of the valuable beans. Surveys in Guatemala indicate that as many as 150 bird species use the traditional plantations shaded by towering native trees, a habitat second only to virgin tropical forests. Half that number inhabit the new cleared plantations.

Not only must Neotropical migrants vie with each other for food and shelter in their southern ranges, they also face competition from the native birds that live there year-round. Some, like the northern waterthrush, defend winter territories in Venezuela just as they defend nest sites in the northern states and Canada. Others join mixed-species flocks, roaming through tropical forests with a strange assemblage of northern and southern birds.

Neotropical migrants face increasing problems at both ends of their long migration flights. Perhaps equally important are "stopover habitats" where they rest and feed along their routes. In spring, colorful songbirds stream northward across the Gulf of Mexico, seeking shelter when they reach the Texas coast. Facing strong head winds or driving rain, they drop into the first vegetation they see along the shore. Wooded sanctuaries like the High Island tracts of the Houston Audubon Society or Sabine Woods owned by the Texas Ornithological Society are vital to their very survival.

Some estimates place the decline in the wood thrush population at 40 percent over twenty-five years, and to lose forever this handsome bird and its ethereal song is unthinkable. As Thoreau wrote, "Whenever a man hears it he is young, and Nature is in her spring." Clearly we cannot preserve every habitat in pristine condition throughout the hemisphere, but international cooperation is the only way to stem the destructive tide.

Texas Tortoise

Gopherus berlandieri

The Texas tortoise has long been one of the trademark animals of the southern portions of our state. Strictly terrestrial, it lumbers slowly along on thickly scaled, strangely elephantine legs. Its high, domed shell is beautifully sculpted by growth rings that encircle each scute (a large scale that, with others, makes up the shell). Unlike most turtles, it may not see water for weeks at a time, and it browses on various grasses and on the pads, flowers and fruits of prickly-pear cactus. Other succulent plants also supplement its vegetarian diet.

One of thirty-nine tortoise species that occur worldwide, the Texas tortoise shares its genus in the United States with two close relatives, the desert tortoise of the Mojave and Sonoran Deserts in the West, and the gopher tortoise of Florida and the extreme southeastern states. All are similar in appearance and habits, and all face similar problems. Each is severely threatened by human disturbance and loss of habitat, as are many other tortoises around the world.

Unlike its eastern and western relatives, the Texas tortoise seldom digs an extensive burrow. Instead, it makes a shallow "pallet" by scraping away vegetation and soil at the base of a bush or cactus, creating a gently sloping ramp in which it rests. This hollow only partially conceals the dormant tortoise but provides some shelter from the scorching midday sun. Occasionally a tortoise may choose to appropriate and modify an old mammal burrow. It is most active in early morning and late afternoon, particularly during hot, dry weather.

Adult males have greatly elongated, forked scutes that curve upward under the head from the plastron, or lower shell. These are used as weapons in courtship battles. During the breeding season, males vie ponderously with each other, pushing and shoving, seeking to get leverage with the strong, forked scutes and turn their rivals on their backs.

Females lay their oval, hard-shelled eggs in shallow chambers dug beneath overhanging bushes. Each may lay a half-dozen or more during a nesting season that lasts from April through September, usually distributing them in more than one site. Babies are less than two inches long at hatching and are brightly marked with yellow at the center of each carapace scute. Texas tortoises grow slowly to reach a maximum shell length of nine inches, and they apparently attain sexual maturity in about fifteen years. Some have been known to live to the age of seventy.

The Texas tortoise traces its ancestry back through the fossil record for at least ten million years to Pliocene deposits in central Texas. Continuation of this ancient lineage, however, seems perilously uncertain today. Once common south of a line from Del Rio to Corpus Christi and extending down into northeastern Mexico, the species is fading from the landscape throughout its range.

Extensively collected for the pet trade, the Texas tortoise was officially listed by the state as a threatened species in 1977. It is illegal to "take, possess, transport, export, sell, or offer for sale" any of these slow-moving, docile reptiles. Tortoises are extremely popular with European collectors, however, and some are probably being exported through Mexico to satisfy that market.

Despite the protective laws, tourists to South Texas still pick up tortoises and take them home as pets. Unfortunately, few survive more than a few weeks or months, quickly succumbing to improper conditions that lead to starvation and disease. Vehicles, too, take a terrible toll, as do imported fire ants that attack hatchling tortoises. Also implicated in many deaths is a pneumonia-like respiratory illness. The disease is readily spread by contact with other turtles and sweeps through captive collections. Someone seeking to return a tortoise to its native habitat may then spread the disease to the wild population.

Dr. Francis Rose of Southwest Texas State University has been studying the Texas tortoise since 1970. On a research site near Port Isabel in South Texas, Rose says, it was possible to find an average of one tortoise every six minutes during the early years of his research. Now he is lucky to find three or four in an entire day.

In an attempt to aid this vanishing turtle, Rose set up a "tortoise ranch" on university property near San Marcos with the aid of the Texas Parks and Wildlife Department. There injured tortoises and those rescued from unauthorized pet owners are treated and housed under proper conditions. None, however, can be released without a careful examination for respiratory disease, and many are destined to remain as permanent residents.

Although many factors have contributed to the decline of Texas' only tortoise, loss of habitat clearly ranks highest on the list. The thorn-scrub forest that formerly covered the Rio Grande Valley has given way to agriculture and development, leaving little room for a turtle that prefers arid grasslands and underbrush.

Nor is the Texas tortoise alone. The ocelot and jaguarundi shared this unique environment, as did the graceful aplomado falcon and countless other wildlife species. Black lace cactus flowered in the brushy grasslands along the coast, and such native plants as Johnston's frankenia, ashy dogweed and slender rush-pea thrived. All now occupy a place on federal and state endangered-species lists, while Walker's manihot is gone completely from the wild.

South Texas is still home to the chachalaca and the green jay, to the Altamira oriole and ringed kingfisher, birds found nowhere else in North America. It is still home, too, to the Texas tortoise, the Texas indigo snake and the Texas horned lizard. But each faces formidable odds in its continuing struggle for survival, and each depends on the preservation of a uniquely Texas habitat.

Attwater's Prairie Chicken

Tympanuchus cupido attwateri

The springtime courtship display of Attwater's prairie chicken ranks as one of nature's greatest spectacles. Males fight for choice positions on the communal lek (courtship site) and patrol their hard-won territories diligently, puffing out their orange neck pouches and dancing in competition for the females. Their feet beat the ground so rapidly they are only a blur; resonant "booming" from the inflated air sacs carries for half a mile in the clear dawn air.

Round and round the birds whirl in the early morning light, sometimes leaping into the air to spar with flashing claws and beaks. The scene is reminiscent of the intricate and colorful ceremonial dances staged by various Native American tribes. Tragically, it is a scene that is becoming all too rare, for Attwater's prairie chicken is the most critically endangered bird in Texas. In spite of determined conservation efforts, the population has continued to decline at a perilous rate. Unless current captive-breeding programs prove successful, this handsome grouse will become extinct within the decade.

Biologists regard Attwater's prairie chicken as a subspecies or race of the greater prairie chicken, a wide-ranging species found on remnant tallgrass prairies across the Midwest and Great Plains. Populations of the latter are also decreasing. Another race, the heath hen, vanished from the East Coast in 1932.

An estimated one million Attwater's prairie chickens once occupied seven million acres of coastal prairie in Texas and Louisiana. Early accounts tell of enormous flocks that darkened the sky. The birds were hunted heavily for food and sport until protected under modern game laws. However, native tallgrass prairies, this bird's essential habitat, have all but vanished from the coastal plain, giving way to steadily increasing urbanization, ranching and agriculture. It is this habitat loss that poses the greatest threat to the remarkable prairie chicken.

Attwater's prairie chicken was officially declared endangered on March 11, 1967, and five years later the 8,000-acre Attwater's Prairie Chicken National Wildlife Refuge was established near Eagle Lake in Colorado County. At that time, a census found 1,772 birds on the Texas coast. By 1988, that number had dropped to 926, and in 1991 there were only 480.

The question is not, "What happened to the prairie chicken?" noted a status report from the federal refuge. Rather, it is "What happened to the prairie?" Only 15,000 acres on portions of two refuges were dedicated to management of the birds — 1/5 of one percent of the original seven-million-acre range. Private ranches harbored small prairie chicken populations, but too little undisturbed prairie remained.

Although the males display in open fields where they are clearly visible, mated females steal away to lay their seven to seventeen spotted eggs amid the tall, concealing native grasses. The downy precocial chicks remain with their mother for several weeks, feeding almost exclusively on insects for the first month and gradually adding seeds, berries and tender leaves to their diet. Unfortunately, biologists have estimated that as few as three birds may survive out of each 100 eggs.

Threats to remnant prairie chicken populations are many. On the few remaining prairie tracts, suppression of fires ended the natural succession of grasses. Trees and brush, once kept under control, crept steadily from stream banks to dot the prairie. The alien Macartney rose, introduced into Texas from Asia in the 1800s as a windbreak for cattle, became an ineradicable pest on hundreds of thousands of acres. Not only do the rose thickets encroach on the birds' prairie habitat, but they also harbor predators such as raccoons and skunks that prey on eggs and young.

Imported fire ants pose a serious threat to hatching prairie chickens and displace other insect species that the chicks require as food. Dr. Nova Silvy of Texas A&M University estimates that the voracious ants have wiped out up to 70 percent of the insect mass and 40 percent of the insect diversity on heavily infested tracts. "There are simply not enough insects left to raise prairie chickens," says Silvy. Cattle egrets, another introduced species, also compete for insect food, and concentrations of ducks and geese bring new diseases and parasites that can be transmitted to the chickens.

Dramatic measures were needed if the Attwater's prairie chicken was to be saved from extinction, and authorities instituted new programs for captive breeding and release. It was hoped the early work could be done with greater prairie chickens in order to establish proper procedures, but there proved to be no time for experimentation. Heavy rains during the nesting seasons from 1991 through 1993 resulted in high mortality, and by 1994 the wild population had dropped to 158 birds in four counties. It plummeted further to only sixty-eight birds in 1995.

Using eggs taken from the wild, personnel at the Houston Zoo, Texas A&M and Fossil Rim Wildlife Center had exceptional success in hatching and raising prairie chickens. Thirteen young birds were radio-collared and released on the Eagle Lake refuge in the summer of 1995. Predators and dehydration took a heavy toll, but three survived the following winter, a creditable result for a grouse release.

The breeding program became even more critical when the 1996 census detected only forty-two birds and no new reproduction in the wild. The San Antonio Zoo joined the other facilities in raising prairie chickens, and funding was obtained from several foundations, societies and industries. The Texas Parks and Wildlife Department instituted an "Adopt-a-Prairie-Chicken" program for individual contributions. More juvenile birds have been released at Eagle Lake and on a Nature Conservancy tract in Galveston County, and captive propagation continues at an increased rate. Public education and sufficient land on which to introduce more birds must also have high priority.

Authorities believe Attwater's prairie chicken can be saved, and the recovery plan calls for the eventual release of 600 birds a year. There is little margin for error, but preliminary results have proved encouraging. A successful captive-breeding program is the last great hope for an otherwise vanishing species.

Certainly no one who has ever seen this unique and handsome prairie chicken in full courtship display would ever question the need for its preservation. Hopefully the prairie chicken will always have a place among the residents of Texas' coastal prairie — a place where males can dance and whirl in the orange light of each new day, a place where females can steal away to incubate their eggs and raise their downy chicks amid the wildflowers and native prairie grasses.

© - Gamini Ratnavira
1997

Houston Toad

Bufo houstonensis

It is a dark, overcast April night in the pine-oak woodlands of Bastrop State Park east of Austin, Texas. A layer of threatening clouds obscures the full moon, and rain seems imminent. A raccoon prowls the shrubby underbrush, its progress marked by rustling leaves. The muffled call of a great horned owl echoes through the forest.

Other sounds, too, punctuate the night—the nocturnal serenades of katydids and crickets and the persistent refrains of tree frogs. Then a rapid, clear, high-pitched trill pierces the darkness. Longer in duration and shriller than the songs of the frogs, it emanates from a shallow, tannin-stained pond. Another voice joins in, and then another. It is a rare chorus unique to east-central Texas and now heard nowhere else in all the world, the mating song of the rare and endangered Houston toad.

Three male toads ring the little pond, each trying with song to attract a mate. One, however, seems to be dominant. He is larger than the others and sings more insistently, his dark throat swelling like a toy balloon as he trills away. The smallest of the trio soon falls silent and hops over to sit beside the singer, acting the role of a "satellite male." Conserving the energy required for singing, he hopes to steal away a receptive female as she approaches.

Mottled brown and gray, with the warty skin characteristic of the genus *Bufo*, the Houston toad looks much like many other

©-GAMINI RATNAVIRA-
1997

of its amphibian relatives. Indeed, it was not described as a separate species until 1953, when it was found to be distinct from the similar and more abundant American and Woodhouse's toads. Because the first specimens were found in the Houston area, the new species took the name of that sprawling city, *Bufo houstonensis*.

Unfortunately, urban development quickly claimed Houston's population of its namesake species. Other suitable habitat on the coastal prairie was cleared for agriculture. Native vegetation gave way to Bermuda grass and croplands. Watershed alteration drained breeding ponds, and the toads were unable to reproduce and survive long-term drought conditions.

The invasion of imported fire ants, too, has undoubtedly contributed to the decline, as it has with many other wildlife species. Newly metamorphosed toadlets are especially vulnerable as they emerge from the ponds that sheltered them as tadpoles. Small and delicate, they are poorly equipped to withstand the voracious, stinging ants that have spread across their range.

One of the first animals to receive protection under the federal Endangered Species Act, the Houston toad was classified as endangered on October 13, 1970. It was also named as one of the most imperiled animals in the United States.

As the coastal populations vanished, Bastrop and Buescher State Parks in Bastrop County and another location in Burleson County remained as the only known sites of this vanishing species. More recently, small numbers of toads have been found in several surrounding counties, but Bastrop State Park remains the population stronghold.

Relatively poor burrowers, these small toads require areas of deep, loose sand or sandy loam in which to hibernate through the winter and aestivate during the periods of hot, dry weather in the summer. The white sands and shallow ponds of Bastrop's "lost pines" region provide the perfect habitat.

After extensive experimentation, the Houston Zoo succeeded in propagating the endangered toad in captivity. The use of ultraviolet lights and simulated heavy rains stimulated mating, and survival rates of the eggs and tadpoles soared. The most perplexing problem, however, was in finding suitable locations in which to release the captive-reared animals. Predators and periodic drought took an enormous toll, thwarting efforts at reintroduction. "What's killing the toad is simply loss of habitat," noted one researcher.

That habitat remains under assault on a number of fronts. Urban sprawl continues unabated, as does clearing of the land for various agricultural purposes. In recent years, conservation groups have fought vehemently against a proposal to enlarge the golf course at Bastrop State Park, the major stronghold of the Houston toad. A compromise recently approved by the National Park Service released funds for that expansion, but it is also slated to help fund additional acreage for the toad.

Few conservation sagas epitomize more fully the pressures placed on wildlife in our modern era. Adapted to a specific environmental niche, and unable to cope with changing conditions, the Houston toad awaits our decision on its future.

KEMP'S RIDLEY SEA TURTLE

Lepidochelys kempii

Five different sea turtles inhabit the Gulf of Mexico and occur sparingly along the Texas coast. Four of those—the Atlantic hawksbill, Kemp's ridley, leatherback and loggerhead—are classified as endangered species. The other, the green sea turtle, is listed as "threatened." Of these, Kemp's ridley ranks as the smallest of the world's sea turtles. It is also the most severely endangered.

Although small by family standards, adult ridleys weigh from seventy-five to 100 pounds. The carapace, or upper shell, measures up to twenty-eight inches across and is more rounded than those of the other species. Young ridleys are dark charcoal gray, turning gradually lighter gray or olive green as they reach adulthood. Their underparts are a pale creamy yellow.

Kemp's ridley normally occurs only in the Gulf of Mexico, although juveniles occasionally wander far northward along the Atlantic seaboard, sometimes reaching Nova Scotia. Moving eastward around Florida, they apparently get caught up in the Gulf Stream and are swept along. Some biologists suspect these "waifs" are lost to the major population; others think they may be able to return.

Little is known about the life of hatchling ridleys, although they seem to spend several months drifting near the surface of the open sea. Adults, on the other hand, prefer the relatively shallow waters of the continental shelf and feed near the bottom. Crabs make up a major portion of their diet, but the turtles also consume shrimp, mollusks, sea urchins, jellyfish, sea stars, fish and marine plants.

A few Kemp's ridleys have nested along the Texas coast, but most come ashore to lay their eggs at Rancho Nuevo, a remote stretch of Gulf beach north of Tampico, Mexico. It is the only major nesting beach of this rare species in the world.

For several weeks before the nesting season, both males and females migrate toward this section of the Gulf for courtship and mating. Then, from late spring into midsummer, the gravid females move closer to the beach. In a seemingly coordinated

©-Gamini Ratnavira
1997

arrival called an "arribada," they emerge from the water and labor mightily across the sand to the elevated dunes above the tidal zone, crawling on limbs flattened into flippers for the aquatic life they normally lead. Digging a hole in the sand, each female deposits her clutch of round, leathery eggs and covers them, then once again returns to the water.

She may lay two or three such clutches during a single season, each containing an average of 100 white eggs. Some females breed again the following year, some not for two years. Meanwhile the males remain at sea. After hatching on the white sand beach, they may never touch land again.

Following nearly two months of incubation in the sun-warmed sand, the eggs hatch and the tiny turtles scramble frantically down the beach and head for the open Gulf. Many will not survive, for birds and other predators scoop them up as quickly as they emerge, while other enemies await them in the sea. Amazingly, the temperature of incubation determines the gender of the hatchling turtles. Higher temperatures give rise primarily to females; lower ones, to males. It is a fascinating trait shared by several turtles and other reptiles.

Sea turtles were once fairly common along the Texas coast and were netted commercially from Matagorda Bay southward during the late nineteenth century. Canneries at Indianola, Fulton, Corpus Christi and Port Isabel converted them to meat and to the highly prized turtle soup that was shipped to cities across the state. By the mid-1890s turtles had become much scarcer and the industry closed, becoming a rare footnote to Texas history.

As late as 1947, tens of thousands of ridley turtles still nested at Rancho Nuevo. Film footage from that year showed an estimated 40,000 females coming ashore in a single day. Their eggs were considered a delicacy, however, and truckloads were dug up and offered for sale in Texas and Mexico. Fewer than 1,000 turtles nest there today. Both juveniles and adults also perished in increasing numbers in the nets of shrimp boats. With its numbers dropping perilously, Kemp's ridley sea turtle was named an endangered species on December 2, 1970.

Under the auspices of the U.S. Fish and Wildlife Service, a novel "headstart program" was instituted in 1978 in an attempt to establish a new nesting area in Texas and increase hatchling survival. Crews along the beach in Mexico caught the eggs as the females laid them and packed them in containers of sand from Padre Island, hoping to imprint in the emerging turtles the smell or chemical composition of that location.

The eggs were then incubated at Padre Island National Seashore and the hatchlings transferred to the National Marine Fisheries Laboratory in Galveston, where they were held for nine to eleven months before release in the offshore Gulf.

Approximately 2,000 turtles were "headstarted" each year until the program failed to win approval for continued licensing and funding in 1993. Despite growing public approval for the fifteen-year project, officials cited a lack of definitive results and a desire to concentrate on protection rather than propagation. The fact that the political climate had changed may also have played a major role.

Kemp's ridleys apparently require ten to twenty years to reach sexual maturity, and they face many hazards along the way. Some die from eating plastic and other trash dumped illegally in the Gulf, but there is strong evidence that shrimp trawling accounts for most mortality. In 1990 a U.S. law was passed requiring shrimp boats to use turtle excluder devices, or TEDs, that guide turtles and other large creatures out of the net through a trap door. Experiments have shown the TEDs work well, but some shrimpers dismantle them or refuse to use them entirely, citing cost and lost catch.

Mortality of Kemp's ridleys continues high along the Texas coast, particularly during the shrimping season, but public awareness may prove the ultimate solution. A Houston-based organization called Help Endangered Animals—Ridley Turtles (HEART), founded in 1982 by conservationist Carole Allen, fought continually for the headstart program and is now working toward other educational goals. A "turtle-safe shrimp" campaign may one day prove as successful as "dolphin-safe tuna."

Meanwhile, recent events on Padre Island are encouraging. Two tagged turtles nested on that beach in 1996. One was hatched in the headstart program in 1983; the other, in 1986. At least nine more nests were found the following summer, offering hope for eventually establishing a Texas breeding colony of Kemp's ridley sea turtles.

Ferruginous Pygmy-Owl

Glaucidium brasilianum

The rays of the rising sun sweep across the coastal prairie, backlighting the tall bluestem and other native grasses glistening with droplets of dew. Then, from deep within a nearby live oak motte, comes the insistent refrain, *took took took*, the low, whistled notes repeated twice a second without pause. It is the call of a ferruginous pygmy-owl, one of the rarest and most charming birds in Texas.

Only six to seven inches long with a wingspan of about fourteen inches, the tiny pygmy-owl weighs no more than three ounces. Perched high in the top of an oak, it is partially hidden by ball-moss and other bromeliads. There it sits unmoving, its bright yellow eyes wary and unblinking. Its upperparts are gray-brown, the crown faintly flecked with white. Light underparts are strongly streaked with reddish brown, and the tail, long for an owl, is reddish with dusky barring. Light spots on the wings blend with the dappled light amid the foliage and epiphytes and add to the effective camouflage. Slowly turning its head, the owl reveals two white-bordered black patches on its nape. *Quatro ojos*, "four eyes," is the name sometimes given the species in Mexico, and the little bird does, indeed, appear to have eyes in the back of its head.

Unlike its close relative, the northern pygmy-owl, which ranges throughout the higher elevations of western North America, the ferruginous pygmy-owl occurs in the U.S. only in the extreme southern portions of Arizona and Texas. It is partial to saguaro deserts and open woodlands in Arizona; in Texas it has been recorded primarily in remnant mesquite and ebony tracts from the Rio Grande Delta upriver to Falcon Dam.

Although birders come to South Texas from across the continent to add this tiny owl to their lists, it can be a frustratingly difficult bird to find. Vital tracts of thornscrub woodland along the river have given way to agricultural fields and trailer parks, threatening not only the pygmy-owl but a host of other plant and animal species that occur nowhere else north of the Rio Grande.

From its outposts along the extreme southern border of the U.S., the ferruginous pygmy-owl ranges southward through the lowlands of Central and South America to the Strait of Magellan. In these lowland tropical forests, it ranks as the most numerous of several small owl species; however, the U.S. population remains very small.

©-Gamini Ratnavira
1997

This unique subspecies is often called the cactus pygmy-owl, *Glaucidium brasilianum cactorum*, and it was proposed for federal listing under the Endangered Species Act on December 12, 1994. That proposal would classify it as "endangered" in Arizona and "threatened" in Texas. Texas' state list already regards it as a threatened species.

Unlike many of its nocturnal relatives, the ferruginous pygmy-owl is chiefly diurnal and is most active at dawn and dusk. A fierce predator in spite of its small size, it consumes a varied diet of insects and other invertebrates, small mammals, birds, reptiles and amphibians. Swooping out from its perch with rapidly beating wings, it attacks with the bullying ferocity of a shrike, gripping its prey with needlelike talons and biting with its razor-sharp bill. The tiny pygmy-owl then flies off with its prize clutched in its talons, sometimes lifting a bird or mammal twice its own weight.

Old woodpecker holes and natural cavities serve as nesting sites for pygmy-owls, which raise only a single brood each year. Three round, white eggs constitute the normal clutch, but some females may lay four or five eggs on the unlined floor of the nest cavity. The male stands guard and brings food while his mate incubates. Hatching occurs in twenty-eight days, and the young fledge about four weeks later. Within a few more days they are capable of capturing large insects and other prey on their own.

Although the ferruginous pygmy-owl has long been regarded as rare and declining in deep South Texas, additional populations have recently been discovered on some of the large private tracts of land that sprawl across the brush country and coastal prairie north of the Rio Grande Valley. Some of these landowners, including the King and Kenedy ranches, are now working with state agencies and private tour companies to host birding and natural-history tours on their property.

The future of Texas conservation depends on such innovative programs. It is no longer possible to save wildlife habitat and our myriad declining species on public lands alone. Development of ecotourism, now the second largest industry in Texas, offers enormous benefits to everyone concerned.

West Indian Manatee

Trichechus manatus

The manatee, so the story goes, was believed by ancient mariners to be a mermaid. Sailors regarded this fabled creature of the deep as half human, half fish—an alluring and seductive beauty forever confined to life in the sea. Modern science has dispelled the myth of the mermaid, but the manatee proves every bit as fascinating. However, it still puzzles and confounds the uninitiated, who often think of it as a giant fish.

In truth, this placid, gentle, and wonderfully droll-looking creature is an air-breathing mammal that nurses its young and has scattered hairs on its tough, leathery skin. In those respects, it resembles common terrestrial mammals, except, of course, that it is adapted for a totally aquatic life.

It is tempting to compare the manatee to the more familiar whales and dolphins, or to the seals and sea lions, but those marine mammals are not close kin. All have simply evolved a similar body shape in response to a common habitat.

The manatee is a member of the scientific order Sirenia, a lineage most biologists believe diverged from the elephants during the Eocene epoch. Fossil remains indicate a gradual adaptation to the watery environment. Similarities in the skull reflect the link to elephants, as does the unusual tooth arrangement. Manatees have an indefinite number of molarlike teeth that erupt in sequence throughout their lives. As the front teeth wear down, they fall out and are replaced by new ones moving forward.

Four living animals occupy the order Sirenia. The species that occurs sparingly in Texas waters is the West Indian manatee, *Trichechus manatus*, an animal that once ranged along the coasts of Florida, Mexico, Central America, the West Indies and the northern portions of South America. It has become very rare or has vanished from most of its former range, and fewer than 3,000 remain along the southern coast of the United States.

The genus *Trichechus* also includes the smaller Amazonian manatee of South America and the West African manatee. The dugong of the Indian and southwestern Pacific Oceans differs from the manatees in having a notched tail more like that of whales. Biologists thus place the dugong in a different family with the extinct Steller's sea cow, an enormous animal weighing up to three tons and adapted for life in the frigid Bering Sea. The latter was

exterminated by hunters less than three decades after its discovery in 1742. Its relatives have fared only slightly better and are likewise threatened with extinction.

The flesh of the sirenians is said to resemble veal, and the hides make excellent leather. Oil from their blubber also served a number of uses. Thus, the defenseless animals were hunted relentlessly. Commercial hunting of the West Indian manatee began in the seventeenth century in the Caribbean, where it was considered a fish by the Spanish church and could be eaten on days of abstinence. Tens of thousands of the placid creatures were killed each year.

Now classified as an endangered species, the manatee is protected under both the Marine Mammal Protection Act of 1972 and the Endangered Species Act of 1973. It has no natural enemies except diseases and unseasonably cold weather. Occasional poaching and senseless vandalism take a small toll, but boats and barges pose the most serious threats to the slow-moving animals in shallow coastal waters. Most bear scars from whirling propellers, and many perish from their wounds each year.

Manatees can live in both fresh and salt water and spend their lives almost completely submerged. They normally frequent large rivers and shallow coves and bays, where they hang suspended below the surface or lie on the bottom to rest. Many sources suggest manatees can stay underwater about fifteen minutes before rising to breathe, but the intervals are usually shorter.

The bones of the manatee are extremely dense, allowing the animal to sink with a full breath of air and remain submerged. Front limbs are modified into flippers that bear flat nails at their tips; there are no hind limbs. The rounded tail is horizontally flattened and functions as an efficient paddle.

Transparent membranes and copious oily secretions protect manatee eyes, while valvular nostrils on the upper surface of the muzzle close underwater. There are no external ears, although hearing is acute. The upper lip is deeply divided, with the two halves functioning separately in working food into the small mouth, a process aided by stiff bristles on the muzzle.

Totally herbivorous, manatees eat both submerged and floating vegetation. In salt water, they subsist primarily on sea grasses; in fresh water they feed on water-hyacinths, hydrilla and other aquatic plants. They apparently consume fifty to 100 pounds a day and may be instrumental in freeing waterways of excess vegetation.

Manatees are not social animals and congregate only in favorite environments or during courtship and mating. Unable to withstand low temperatures, they often assemble at warm springs during the winter months. Most of the U.S. population resides in Florida's coastal waters, but manatees have been seen occasionally along the Texas coast.

One such wanderer delighted throngs of watchers in Houston, Texas, in late November and early December, 1995. Against all odds, this wayward marine mammal crossed Galveston Bay, ascended the busy Houston Ship Channel, dodged ships from around the world, and finally found sanctuary in Buffalo Bayou at the outfall of a city water-treatment facility. There it remained for several days as crowds of people lined the bayou banks from dawn till dark to watch its aquatic antics. Most had never seen a manatee; a significant number had never even heard of such an animal. Every local media outlet covered the unfolding story, and Houston's most famous resident was quickly dubbed Hou-manatee.

With a December cold front bearing down, wildlife agents feared for the manatee's health and hoped it would leave under its own power. Indeed, it ventured downstream several times, only to return repeatedly to the warm-water discharge from the treatment plant. A floating "salad bar" filled with water-hyacinths, romaine lettuce and cabbage provided supplemental food, but officials finally decided to capture the famous bayou resident.

It was not an easy task. Manatee experts and a veterinarian from Florida joined federal and state personnel from several agencies in the complex effort. On their second try, the manatee was encircled with a long net, wrestled to the bank and carefully lifted by crane to a foam pad, all under the watchful eyes of a cheering crowd and a battery of television cameras.

Hou-manatee proved to be a 10 1/2-foot, 1,252-pound adult female and was renamed Sweet Pea. Trucked to Sea World of Texas in San Antonio for further tests, she was then flown aboard a Coast Guard plane to Florida and released in the warm, crystal waters of Homosassa Springs State Park with other manatees.

Texans will not soon forget their rare visitor, and for those few days in 1995, Houston's Buffalo Bayou served as an unparalleled environmental classroom. Seeing a manatee for the first time, one viewer commented, "It sure is ugly." Others exclaimed excitedly, "It's beautiful!" This one huge, gentle marine mammal charmed an entire city and made a powerful statement for the protection and preservation of our vanishing wildlife heritage.

Sperm Whale

Physeter macrocephalus

Few casual visitors to the Texas coast realize that a wide variety of marine mammals reside offshore. Except for the common bottlenose dolphin found in the bays and estuaries, most are seldom seen from land. Surprisingly, at least twenty-nine species in the scientific order Cetacea—the whales, dolphins, and porpoises—have been documented in the Gulf of Mexico, and the majority of those have been observed in Texas waters. Many records come from strandings of sick or disoriented cetaceans along our beaches, a mystery we still do not fully understand.

Most numerous of the Gulf's great whales is the sperm whale, although blue, fin, humpback, minke, Bryde's and northern right whales have all been reported on rare occasions. So, too, have many smaller species. Among these giants of the deep are the largest creatures, past or present, that have ever lived on Earth.

With its huge, truncated, boxlike head, the sperm whale is also one of the most distinctive of the cetaceans. Its single blowhole is located far forward on the left edge of the square snout, and the resulting plume as the animal breathes is projected forward and to the left. Even when the sperm whale floats low in the water, its shape and the characteristic spout are immediately recognizable. This was the image in which author Herman Melville created Captain Ahab's great white nemesis, Moby Dick.

The sperm whale was once the prime target of the pelagic whaling industry. Whale oil was used for lamps and lubricants, while the waxy spermaceti contained in the massive forehead made excellent smokeless candles. In the mid-1800s, cannon-mounted harpoons replaced more primitive hand weapons, and in the early 1920s, floating factory ships began processing whales at sea. Several species were taken in enormous numbers, and it is amazing they survived at all.

Countries around the world finally agreed on a whaling ban in 1986, but many animals are still killed each year. A loophole in the ban allows any nation to take whales for "scientific research," and the meat and oil may then be processed for commercial use.

The sperm whale, along with many of the other great whales, is now classified as endangered under U.S. federal statutes. Most marine mammals found in Texas waters are also on the state list of endangered or threatened species.

While most of the larger whales feed by straining marine organisms through fringed plates of baleen, or "whale bone," that hang from the upper jaw, the sperm whale is a "toothed whale" more closely related to the dolphins. The lower jaw is strangely small and slender, but it bears twenty-two to twenty-four large, conical teeth along each side.

Throwing its broad, triangular flukes high in the air, the sperm whale dives almost straight down into the ocean depths, sometimes descending more than 3,000 feet below the surface. Indeed, some biologists believe it may be capable of diving to 10,000 feet. There, in the inky blackness, it pursues the large squid that make up the bulk of its diet, occasionally adding various shellfish, jellyfish and finned fish for variety. How the whale finds its prey in the submarine darkness remains a mystery, but one theory suggests that the sonarlike series of clicking sounds used in echolocation may also aid in the search for food.

Although a typical feeding dive lasts for about forty-five minutes, a sperm whale can remain submerged for as long as two hours. With all its aquatic skill, however, it is still an air-breathing mammal, and it must eventually return to the surface or drown. There the moisture-laden air it expels from its lungs cools and condenses into the characteristic spout.

An adult male sperm whale may reach a length of sixty feet and weigh as much as fifty tons; the female is considerably smaller, with a proportionately smaller, more rounded head. Even a newborn calf may be twelve to fourteen feet long and weigh more than a ton.

Sperm whales apparently reach sexual maturity in about ten years, and a complete breeding cycle may be as long as five to seven years. After a gestation period of fifteen months, the cow nurses her calf for up to two years and then waits a year or more before mating once again.

Sperm whales have been found in all the oceans of the world, including frigid Arctic and Antarctic waters. For the most part, however, they inhabit the warmer temperate and tropical portions of the Atlantic and Pacific. Solitary males migrate toward higher latitudes in summer, sometimes reaching the fringes of the polar ice, but they then return to warmer seas where groups of more social females remain. Each dominant male competes with others for a harem of twenty to thirty females, while smaller males assemble elsewhere in nonbreeding "bachelor groups."

Sperm whales and other large cetaceans rank among the most magnificent animals on Earth. It seems almost a miracle they have survived the onslaught through the ages, but their future is far from assured. Hopefully, given full protection, and spared the pollution and depredation of our oceans, they will continue to swim off Texas shores.

Mexican Wolf

Canis lupus baileyi

Few creatures epitomize more fully the sense of wildness and nature's great mystique than the Mexican wolf. To look into its piercing eyes is to hark back to a day when these animals roamed an untamed land, when their primeval chorus drifted across the plains and echoed from the rocky hillsides. Those sights and sounds are now gone from Texas, and only a successful reintroduction program can bring them back. Not everyone looks with favor on the wolf's return, however, engendering heated debate about the ultimate fate of this handsome animal.

The Mexican wolf, *Canis lupus baileyi*, is a southern subspecies of the widespread gray wolf, or timber wolf, which has been persecuted throughout its range. The Mexican wolf was placed on the federal list of endangered species in 1976, joining the eastern timber wolf, *C. l. lycaon*, and the northern Rocky Mountain gray wolf, *C. l. irremotus.*

Larger than the coyote, and with a proportionately larger head and broader muzzle, the wolf normally has grayish upperparts heavily washed with black, although some individuals are much darker than others. Males may occasionally reach a weight of 180 pounds; females are somewhat smaller.

Wolves mate for life and make their dens in holes dug into the hillsides or seek shelter in crevices in rocky bluffs. There the female gives birth to four to seven young in late winter or early spring. Born naked, blind, and helpless, the pups grow rapidly and are nearly full-grown by the following October.

Wolves once ranged across the western two-thirds of Texas, where they traveled and hunted in small packs centered around family groups. Those inhabiting the prairies and plains originally depended on the bison herds for food, while others preyed on deer and pronghorns. When larger game was scarce, they hunted rabbits, ground squirrels and even mice.

Settlers advancing across the state spelled trouble for the widespread wolf.

Domestic livestock replaced bison and pronghorns on the landscape, and there seemed little difference to canine eyes. According to Robin Doughty in *Wildlife and Man in Texas*, ranchers in the mid-1850s set out poisoned carcasses for wolves, used dogs to track them down, dug them out of dens and shot every individual on sight.

Noted Texas author J. Frank Dobie wrote that one test of a ranchhand's ability was to run down a lobo; however, because of the wolf's amazing endurance, not many could do this without breaking down their horses. Most early Texans called the Mexican wolf simply "lobo"; the smaller coyote was the "prairie wolf" or the "coyote wolf." The red wolf, or "black wolf," replaced those two species in the eastern portions of the state. None was especially popular with ranchers or farmers.

Biologist Vernon Bailey's 1905 report for the U.S. Biological Survey on his travels in Texas claimed that "the big lobo is still common over most of the plains and mountain country of western Texas." Popular folklore to the contrary, humans had little to fear from the wild wolves. Livestock proved fair game, however, and the crusade against lobo continued. Cowhands even crawled into dens to shoot the females and their pups.

A government campaign of trapping and poisoning was initiated in 1915, using federal funds augmented by additional support from the state, several counties and various stockmen's clubs. During the fiscal year ending in June, 1919, according to Doughty, an average of twenty-seven federal hunters and fifteen other men hired with independent funds were employed in "predator control." In that year they killed "5 cougars, 30 lobo wolves, 212 red or timber wolves, 2,502 coyotes, 474 bobcats, and an assortment of other carnivores, including 13 'stock-killing dogs' and 5 house cats."

Totals peaked in 1939, when more than 20,000 predators—mostly wolves, coyotes and cougars—were killed. Few people in those days gave any thought to the fact that wolves played a valuable role in the natural selection of big-game animals, and several localities in Texas suffered serious problems with a resulting overpopulation of deer.

In 1945, cyanide guns were developed, and the battle escalated. These "humane wildlife getters" added a new dimension to the predator-control wars that lasted through the mid-1960s.

The last authenticated reports of Mexican wolves in Texas, according to Davis and Schmidly in *The Mammals of Texas*, occurred in December of 1970. One male was shot on a large ranch south of Alpine in Brewster Country, and a few days later another was poisoned on a ranch east of

Marathon. Subsequent reports of free-ranging wolves in Texas almost certainly involve large feral dogs or coyote-dog hybrids.

Nationally, the captive population of Mexican wolves totaled a mere thirty-nine wolves in 1990, but a successful breeding program increased the number to 148 by 1997. They are held in two dozen different zoos and other facilities across the U.S. and Mexico, and the U.S. Fish and Wildlife Service is charged with their preservation. The listed objectives of the recovery plan call for maintaining a captive breeding program while also reintroducing wolves into the wild to "reestablish a population of at least 100 Mexican wolves within their historic range." The latter has been slow in coming, and conservation groups have sued to speed up the process.

In March 1998, the U. S. Fish and Wildlife Service introduced eleven Mexican wolves from captive stock into the Apache National Forest in southeastern Arizona. Two additional wolves were released later that year and twenty-one in 1999. Of the thirty-four wolves released, five were shot, one disappeared, one was hit by a vehicle, and five were returned to captivity. Twenty-two radio collared Mexican wolves, and an estimate of eight more without radio collars were free-ranging by 2001, indicating there are now Mexican wolves that were born in the wild, having never been in capitivity.

Many have suggested releasing wolves on public lands in the Big Bend region of West Texas, but an uproar from ranchers and local politicians has been heard in a series of public meetings. There are, as yet, no firm plans to reintroduce the Mexican wolf on Texas soil.

In spite of proposals to allow ranchers to shoot and kill wolves in the act of attacking livestock or to compensate them for their loss, opposition remains unchecked. "You don't release one of the most cunning and lethal predators," one rancher raged, while a county judge suggested that "this is nothing less than environmental imperialism."

The only place the wolf can win the battle for survival is in the court of public opinion, and environmental groups such as The Mexican Wolf Coalition of Texas are working steadily to that end. A pair of wolves on display in an interpretive exhibit at the Houston Zoo will help educate people to their role in our environment. Through efforts such as these, hope remains that the Mexican wolf may once again roam wild across Texas and the Desert Southwest.

Bald Eagle

Haliaeetus leucocephalus

Peregrine Falcon

Falco peregrinus

It was on June 20, 1782, that the U.S. Congress approved the "American eagle" as our national emblem. The designer of the seal originally proposed using the image of the golden eagle, but others noted that it had served for centuries on the seals and flags of several European states. Instead, Congress chose the bald eagle, which occurs only in North America.

Its white head and tail and its massive yellow bill make the adult bald eagle immediately recognizable. Immatures, however, are mostly dark, with irregular white patches in the wings and at the base of the tail. They do not gain adult plumage until their fourth year. The common name comes from the Old English *balde*, meaning white, and the scientific name reflects the same striking feature. *Haliaeetus* is Greek for sea eagle, while *leucocephalus* means white head.

The wings of the male span seven feet; those of the larger female, nearly eight. Sailing aloft on those broad, flat wings, bald eagles range along our coasts and inland near lakes and rivers. They feed primarily on fish but also take small mammals and waterfowl. Carrion provides a supplement to that diet, particularly for young and inexperienced birds during the harsh winter months.

Bald eagles establish long-term pair bonds, and many apparently mate for life. Their shrill cries echo across the landscape as they perform spectacular aerial courtship displays, locking talons and somersaulting toward the ground.

The mated pair returns to the same breeding site year after year, adding new material to the stick nest each season until it reaches incredible proportions. One such nest proved to be nearly ten feet across and twenty feet deep. Another weighed more than two tons. Perched high in the tops of trees, these enormous structures occasionally plummet to earth as the trees snap under the weight.

The female lays from one to three large bluish white eggs; the normal clutch is two. Incubation begins with the first egg so that the chicks hatch at different times. The first to hatch has an obvious advantage, and the second often dies. Incubation requires thirty-four to thirty-six days, with both parents taking part, and the young are nearly three months old before they leave the security of the nest.

Despite its honored and symbolic status, the bald eagle has been severely persecuted through the years; its very survival has been a long and uphill battle. Not until 1940 did it gain full protection from the Bald Eagle Protection Act. Even then, habitat loss contributed to a severe population decline, as did environmental contamination by pesticides and heavy-metal residues. In 1967, under a law that preceded the Endangered Species Act of 1973, our nation's symbol was officially declared endangered.

The toxic and persistent pesticide DDT was strongly implicated in reproductive failure of the bald eagle. Egg shells grew progressively thinner and broke beneath the weight of incubating birds; other eggs con-

© Gamini Ratnavira
1997

tained malformed chicks that subsequently died. In 1972, in a bold stroke by the fledgling U.S. Environmental Protection Agency, the controversial decision was made to ban the use of DDT within this country. It was a monumental step in the preservation of several vanishing species.

Since that date, America's bald eagle has staged a slow but steady comeback and was officially downlisted from "endangered" to "threatened" in August, 1995. According to a survey published by the Environmental Defense Fund in June of 1997, eagles have increased from 500 breeding pairs in 1963 to a current total of more than 5,000 pairs throughout the lower forty-eight states.

Another beneficiary of the ban on DDT was the peregrine falcon, *Falco peregrinus*. The peregrine's worldwide range is more extensive than that of any other bird, encompassing all of the continents except Antarctica and many of the oceanic island groups. Indeed, this sleek, elegant raptor was once called "the world's most successful flying bird." It is also one of the fastest, reaching an estimated 150 to 200 miles per hour in a dive and maintaining speeds of sixty miles per hour in flat, powered flight. It subsists primarily on a diet of birds, which it captures on the wing.

The adult peregrine falcon is a bluish gray above, while its pale underparts are heavily barred with gray. Most distinctive is a black cap that extends in broad wedges, often called "mustaches," below the eyes. The effect is not unlike an old-fashioned aviator's helmet, appropriate attire for this master of the skies.

Speed could not save the peregrine from the ravages of pesticides, however, and by the mid-1960s none were breeding east of the Mississippi River. The entire eastern population had been extirpated, and only 324 pairs could be found across the continent. The ban on DDT has contributed to a slow recovery, as have captive-breeding and reintroduction programs. The peregrine has repopulated much of its former U.S. range, and on August 26, 1998, notice to "delist" the bird was published in the *Federal Register*. However, the peregrine remains in peril throughout many portions of the world.

A few peregrines nest in the rugged Chisos, Davis and Guadalupe Mountains of Trans-Pecos Texas and in the canyons along the Rio Grande, where they remain throughout the year. Most seen within the boundaries of the state, however, are from northern populations that breed in Arctic Alaska and Canada. These falcons move along the Texas coast in spring and fall, often assembling on Padre Island and other barrier beaches to put on fat reserves for their long journey. They spend the winter months as far south as Argentina.

Bald eagles, too, inhabit Texas. Many are winter visitors from the North, but some are permanent, year-round residents, nesting along the coastal plain and on some of the larger wooded lakes and reservoirs in the eastern portions of the state. In 1995, there were forty active eagle nests in more than thirty counties, a vast improvement from a meager seven nests in 1971.

The majestic bald eagle and the sleek peregrine falcon have rebounded from the brink of extinction, although their survival is by no means secure. The greatest challenge for the future lies in preventing further habitat destruction, thereby preserving their place in Texas skies.

Red Wolf

Canis rufus

The red wolf once ranged from central Texas eastward along the Gulf Coast to Florida and Georgia and through the Mississippi Valley to central Illinois and Indiana. Some reports suggest it may actually have occurred as far northward as Pennsylvania.

During the twentieth century, however, the species rapidly gave way to habitat loss, predator-control projects and "genetic swamping" by interbreeding with an expanding population of coyotes. By the 1960s, only a few remained along the upper Texas coast and in adjacent Louisiana. A short time later the red wolf was declared "biologically extinct" in the wild; however, a small group was maintained in captive-breeding facilities. The descendants of those last wild-born wolves are now being reintroduced at suitable sites across the South.

The red wolf has long been something of a taxonomic mystery. Some suggested it was merely a subspecies of the more broadly distributed gray wolf, while others asserted it was a form of coyote. Most biologists now agree, however, that it deserves full species status. A small, slender wolf normally weighing from forty to eighty pounds, it has unusually long legs adapted for long-distance running. The typical red wolf resembles the coyote in color, but some individuals are more blackish. Indeed, many early Texas settlers called it the "black wolf."

The red wolf has a proportionately more massive head and broader muzzle than the coyote, which has a somewhat pointed profile. There are also differences in the skull structure that can be detected on preserved specimens or by X-ray techniques on living animals. The latter proved useful in determining genetic purity during the struggle to save the red wolf from total extinction. As Susan Middleton and David Littschwager pointed out in *Witness: Endangered Species of North America*, it is ironic that we once doggedly pursued the wolf, trying to rid it from the face of the earth, and now we work just as tirelessly for its return.

Unusually shy creatures, red wolves traveled in small groups of two or three and frequently hunted alone. They lacked the complex social structure of the larger gray wolf packs but were more sociable than coyotes. Red wolves originally inhabited the brushy and wooded areas of central and eastern Texas as well as the coastal prairie. They dug their cave-like dens on the slopes or crests of low, sandy hills or in the banks of irrigation and drainage ditches. Later, they also used culverts and drain pipes. The two to six pups were born in spring and reared by both parents.

Rabbits, rats and mice, prairie chickens and other birds, and occasional deer were staples of the red wolf's natural diet. Coastal populations utilized fish and crabs as well. After their introduction to the region, nutria also proved popular as prey. Like others of their family, red wolves were most active at night and were not above incursions on farmers' livestock, especially free-ranging pigs. Those habits inevitably led to the same unceasing control measures inflicted on the Mexican wolf, coyote, cougar, bobcat and other predators within the state.

Most biologists agree, however, that the major reason for the sharp and sudden decline of the red wolf was its genetic mixing with the coyote. It literally bred itself out of existence in the wild.

Before settlers moved across Texas, coyotes were restricted to the western grasslands and red wolves to more heavily wooded habitats. The coyotes then moved into areas opened by clearing of the timberlands, and the two species began to interact. Starting on the Edwards Plateau at the turn of the century, according to Davis and Schmidly in *The Mammals of Texas*, decreasing wolf populations began to interbreed with the increasing number of coyotes, and the "hybrid swarm" moved eastward. By the early 1960s, the only purebred red wolves remaining inhabited the Texas coastal prairie in Chambers, Liberty and Jefferson Counties. A few years later, Anahuac National Wildlife Refuge was one of the last sanctuaries of a vanishing species.

The timely passage of the Endangered Species Act of 1973 enabled the U.S. Fish and Wildlife Service to move in and capture the remaining wolves. The animals deemed most genetically pure were sent to a newly constructed breeding facility at the Point Defiance Zoological Gardens in Tacoma, Washington. There, in 1977, four litters of pups were born, increasing by a precious fourteen animals the world's supply of red wolves. Success came none too soon, for field activities were concluded in 1980, when the red wolf was deemed to be extinct in its native habitat.

Other zoos and nature centers across the country joined the effort of maintaining and breeding red wolves and educating the public as to their plight. One of the first such facilities was the Texas Zoo in Victoria, which harbors a wide variety of wildlife native to the state.

In 1987, four pairs of adult red wolves were released at Alligator River National Wildlife Refuge on an island off the coast of North Carolina. This monumental event marked the first time in the United States that an endangered species previously deemed extinct in the wild was returned to its former range. It was also the first reintroduction of a predatory animal. A total of forty-two wolves were released on the refuge between 1987 and 1992, and at least twenty-three new pups were born, making up for a portion of the inevitable casualties.

Other red wolves have subsequently been released on Bull Island in South Carolina, St. Vincent Island in Florida, and Horn Island in Mississippi. The most recent reintroduction was in Great Smoky Mountains National Park, the first inland site.

Unfortunately, as noted by Davis and Schmidly, "It is doubtful red wolves can be reintroduced in Texas because of human population pressures where they formerly occurred." Perhaps someday that, too, can be accomplished, but at least for now the offspring of Texas red wolves once again roam wild.

Wood Stork

Mycteria americana

One of the largest of our wading birds, the wood stork has a wingspread of more than five feet. With its stiltlike legs and long neck, it might be confused with the more abundant herons and egrets with which it paces the marshes along the Texas coast. In flight, however, storks hold their necks outstretched like cranes, while herons and their close relatives pull their necks back in a graceful S-curve, heads resting on their shoulders.

The wood stork was formerly called the "wood ibis," a name no longer in use. It is not related to the ibises and is, in fact, a true stork, the only one found regularly in North America. Another stork species, the even larger jabiru, has occurred only a few times as a very rare straggler to southern Texas from Central and South America.

Black trailing edges of the wings and black tail contrast sharply with the otherwise white plumage of the wood stork. It is the head and bill that are most distinctive, however. The massive beak is nearly ten inches long, thick and slightly downcurved, a remarkable appendage that gives our stork its scientific name, *Mycteria americana*. *Mykter* is the Greek word for snout.

Young birds have feathered heads, but they become progressively more bald as they near adulthood. In maturity, the head and upper neck are entirely naked and dark, dusky gray or black. Clearly, the wood stork will win no awards for its classic profile, but what it lacks in facial beauty, it more than makes up for in grace on the wing. It flies with ponderous elegance, neck and legs extended, huge wings flapping slowly and rhythmically. Catching the thermals on a hot summer afternoon, a flock of storks may soar upward in sweeping spirals until lost from sight among the clouds.

Named for its penchant for nesting and roosting in trees, the wood stork is a summer visitor to Texas, wandering northward in family groups or small flocks after the breeding season in the tropics. It occurs mainly along the coast, where it stalks slowly and deliberately through the marshes and shallow ponds, feeding on almost anything it can catch. Fish, crabs, crayfish, small snakes, turtles, frogs and large insects are all grabbed in the half-open beak, which the stork swings methodically from side to side in the water.

Historically, wood storks bred from South Carolina southward along the Atlantic Coast and around the Gulf of Mexico to Texas, with the largest colonies and greatest numbers in the cypress swamps of Florida. Displaced by the logging and draining of the swamps, the channelization of rivers and bayous, and an increase in pollution and pesticides, the population slowly dwindled. From an estimated 20,000 pairs in the 1930s, it decreased to 11,000 in 1960 and fewer than 5,000 pairs by 1980. The wood stork was formally listed as a federally endangered species in February, 1984.

Ironically, our only stork did not suffer the fate of many other wildlife species. Its unpalatable flesh saved it from market hunters and the cooking pot, and its unfeathered head precluded the plume hunting that decimated egret populations. The regal birds could not, however, cope with massive habitat destruction. Disturbance led to nesting failures, and changing water levels made feeding difficult.

Wood storks are primarily tactile feeders, swinging their sensitive beaks back and forth and quickly snapping up anything with which they come in contact. Tests have shown that this "snap reflex" is triggered in less than twenty-five milliseconds, leaving a careless fish no time to escape. Such a feeding mechanism requires a high concentration of fish or other aquatic creatures, a resource that was gradually depleted. Although some birds were found to fly as far as eighty miles from their nests to fertile feeding grounds, many simply abandoned their colonies as habitat declined.

Once found nesting regularly in the eastern portions of our state, the wood stork has been gone as a breeding resident for several decades. Recently, however, there have been reports of the return of this tall, stately bird to the swamps of East Texas. Perhaps, with continued preservation of wetlands and the banning of persistent pesticides, the wood stork will be back. Hopefully it can join the swallow-tailed kite, the bald eagle and the osprey as majestic birds that have slowly returned from the brink of extinction to once again nest in Texas.

MEXICAN WOLF

Canis lupus baileyi

Few creatures epitomize more fully the sense of wildness and nature's great mystique than the Mexican wolf. To look into its piercing eyes is to hark back to a day when these animals roamed an untamed land, when their primeval chorus drifted across the plains and echoed from the rocky hillsides. Those sights and sounds are now gone from Texas, and only a successful reintroduction program can bring them back. Not everyone looks with favor on the wolf's return, however, engendering heated debate about the ultimate fate of this handsome animal.

The Mexican wolf, *Canis lupus baileyi*, is a southern subspecies of the widespread gray wolf, or timber wolf, which has been persecuted throughout its range. The Mexican wolf was placed on the federal list of endangered species in 1976, joining the eastern timber wolf, *C. l. lycaon*, and the northern Rocky Mountain gray wolf, *C. l. irremotus*.

Larger than the coyote, and with a proportionately larger head and broader muzzle, the wolf normally has grayish upperparts heavily washed with black, although some individuals are much darker than others. Males may occasionally reach a weight of 180 pounds; females are somewhat smaller.

Wolves mate for life and make their dens in holes dug into the hillsides or seek shelter in crevices in rocky bluffs. There the female gives birth to four to seven young in late winter or early spring. Born naked, blind, and helpless, the pups grow rapidly and are nearly full-grown by the following October.

Wolves once ranged across the western two-thirds of Texas, where they traveled and hunted in small packs centered around family groups. Those inhabiting the prairies and plains originally depended on the bison herds for food, while others preyed on deer and pronghorns. When larger game was scarce, they hunted rabbits, ground squirrels and even mice.

Settlers advancing across the state spelled trouble for the widespread wolf.

Pantropical Spotted Dolphin

Stenella attenuata

Almost everyone is familiar with the most abundant of Texas' marine mammals, the bottlenose dolphin, *Tursiops truncatus*. It is the star of several aquarium "porpoise" shows and has been featured in numerous movies and television programs. Aerial surveys estimate a population of 35,000 to 45,000 of these common cetaceans in the Gulf of Mexico, and many of them inhabit the shallow bays, estuaries and ship channels along the Texas coast. Another population remains in the deeper offshore waters, and there is apparently little interaction between the two.

The bottlenose dolphin, however, is by no means the only species recorded from Texas waters. Davis and Schmidly, in *The Mammals of Texas*, list nine different dolphins as well as several other small, toothed whales. Most are restricted to the deeper regions of the Gulf of Mexico, and many take their place on the list of our state's fauna because of occasional strandings along the shore.

Although these animals are frequently called porpoises, they are, in fact, more properly named dolphins. "Whale" is an all-inclusive term that may be used to describe any cetacean, although it is usually applied to the larger species. Dolphins are small whales with distinctly narrowed snouts, or beaks, and with numerous conical teeth. Porpoises, on the other hand, are small, blunt-nosed whales that lack the beak and have flat, spade-shaped teeth. By these definitions, no porpoises are known to occur in Texas waters.

One of the rarer dolphins found along our coast is the pantropical spotted dolphin, *Stenella attenuata*. According to Davis and Schmidly, three individuals were found beached on Padre Island during Hurricane Fern in 1971, and two were stranded near Port Aransas in 1989 and 1990.

A small dolphin with a relatively short beak, it has a blackish back, lighter gray sides and white underparts. The fins and flukes are black. Most distinctive are the small black spots that cover the pale sides and abdomen and the contrasting grayish dots that fleck the dark back. However, the amount of spotting varies with age and within different populations. Newborn calves are unspotted, while older animals are the most strongly marked.

The pantropical spotted dolphin, as its name implies, ranges throughout the tropical and subtropical oceans of the world. It is particularly common around tropical islands, but it also follows ships and smaller boats, riding the bow waves and foraging for the fish that make up the major portion of its diet. An active, acrobatic animal, it sometimes leaps high into the air, dropping back into the water with a resounding splash. It is usually seen in pods of five to thirty animals, but large groups of more than a thousand have occasionally been observed.

Little is known about the reproductive habits of the pantropical spotted dolphin in the Gulf of Mexico. Studies in the Pacific, however, suggest that males reach sexual maturity at about six years of age; females, at five. Gestation lasts eleven and a half months, and the mother nurses her calf for another eleven months. Thus the interval between calves is usually more than two years.

Once combined with the Atlantic spotted dolphin under the scientific name *Stenella frontalis*, the pantropical spotted dolphin has now been given full species status. It is distinguished from *frontalis* by its smaller size, narrower beak and darker upperparts. Its teeth are also smaller and more numerous.

The Atlantic form is confined to the Atlantic Ocean system and also occurs in the Gulf of Mexico and off the Texas coast. Indeed, it ranks second to the bottlenose dolphin in abundance in the Gulf.

Along with the bottlenose, Atlantic and pantropical spotted dolphins, Texas can claim the rough-toothed, common, Risso's, Clymene, striped and spinner dolphins. Also recorded within state waters are such small cetaceans as the pygmy and dwarf sperm whales; Blainville's, Gervais' and Cuvier's beaked whales; the killer, false killer and pygmy killer whales; and the short-finned pilot and melon-headed whales.

Much of what we know about the presence of these animals comes from information gathered by the Texas Marine Mammal Stranding Network organized in 1980. This volunteer network consists of scientists, students, state and federal agencies, veterinarians and interested individuals who assist stranded animals, giving treatment to those that live and obtaining scientific data on those that fail to survive.

The offshore waters of the Gulf of Mexico are home to many marine mammals seldom seen by those of us confined to shore. All are protected by strict federal laws, but each can be seriously affected by human activities. Petroleum production and transportation, heavy shipping and boating traffic, and pollution of the Gulf waters all pose potential problems.

In the Pacific, enormous numbers of pantropical spotted dolphins have been killed incidentally during tuna-seining operations. In 1970, some 400,000 dolphins were killed by U.S. vessels alone, but that figure has been steadily reduced. Stronger laws and a voluntary mortality-reduction program are now in effect, and an international agreement has as its goal a reduction of the total incidental catch to less than 5,000 dolphins per year. Even that, of course, seems a terrible toll.

Although the problem with incidental catching of dolphins has never been as serious in the Gulf of Mexico, many of Texas' diverse marine mammals face an uncertain future. Increased human activities and a low reproductive rate place these fascinating and highly intelligent creatures continually at risk.

TEXAS HORNED LIZARD

Phrynosoma cornutum

In 1993, the Texas legislature designated the Texas horned lizard as the official state reptile. "The horned lizard possesses numerous attributes that qualify it as an official representative of our state," the House Concurrent Resolution stated. "Despite a spiny exterior that presents a forbidding appearance, it is at heart a docile and peaceful creature...well known and much loved by its human neighbors." Unfortunately the resolution also noted that "like many other things truly Texan, it is a threatened species."

Indeed, the horned lizard, once abundant across much of the state, has disappeared from large portions of its former range. It now occupies a place on the Texas Parks and Wildlife Department's list of threatened animals, and it is illegal to collect, possess or remove a Texas horned lizard from its habitat.

Known to most Texans as the "horned toad" or "horny toad," or to alumni of Texas Christian University as their revered mascot, the "horned frog," this fascinating animal is in truth a reptile rather than an amphibian. Unlike most lizards, however, it has a round, warty body and a short, stubby tail. This curious appearance probably accounts for the misnomers.

More than a dozen species of horned lizards occur from southern Canada to Guatemala, each identified by the number and placement of spines at the back of the head and the rows of fringe scales along the sides of the body. Seven species inhabit the United States. Texas hosts three different members of the genus *Phrynosoma*, the most widespread of which is appropriately named the Texas horned lizard. It originally ranged from Kansas and Oklahoma through virtually all of the state and southward into Mexico, and from sea level to an elevation of at least 6,000 feet. The two central head spines are much larger than the other spines, and two rows of prominent scales fringe the sides of the body. Colors vary with the individual, but most horned lizards are reddish or yellowish brown with darker spots. Like many other lizards, however, they magically change their hues in response to the stimuli of heat and light.

Two other species, the roundtail horned lizard (*P. modestum*) and the mountain short-horned lizard (*P. douglassii hernandesi*), also occur in Texas. The former inhabits the deserts in the western portions of the state, while the latter occupies the rocky pinyon-juniper slopes of the Davis, Guadalupe and Hueco Mountains. This short-horned lizard is also protected as a threatened species in Texas.

The cryptic pattern and irregular outline of the horned lizard provide amazingly effective camouflage, and the reptile can be extremely difficult to spot. Approached too closely, it scurries off at a surprisingly rapid pace, abruptly stopping again to flatten its body against the ground, where it blends perfectly with its surroundings. The spiny exterior undoubtedly provides further protection against predators; and that defense becomes even more formidable as the horned lizard inflates its body like a miniature balloon, presenting a hungry foe with a cactuslike array of spines that proves difficult to swallow. When all other methods of defense fail, the lizard's eyelids suddenly swell and thin streams of blood shoot from tiny openings near the corners of its eyes. In addition to startling an aggressor, the blood apparently contains noxious compounds that send the would-be predator slinking quickly away.

In spite of these protective mechanisms, the Texas horned lizard often falls prey to roadrunners, hawks, shrikes, snakes, coyotes, foxes and other large mammalian predators. Unfortunately, these defenses also do not protect the strange little animal from human interference. Countless horned lizards were sold as pets across the country, sometimes under such fanciful names as "miniature dinosaur" or "dwarf dragon." Others were picked up and carried home by tourists visiting the state, usually to die a lingering death from improper care. Fortunately these practices have now been made illegal by the Texas horned lizard's protected status.

Texas horned lizards feed on a variety of spiders, sowbugs and insects, but ants make up a major portion of the diet. Especially favored are the large red harvester ants, which live in underground nests surrounded by areas that are meticulously cleared of all plant growth and debris. However, harvesters and many of our other native ant species have been displaced by the more aggressive alien fire ants. The horned lizards have suffered in large part due to the loss of habitat, pesticide spraying and the accidental introduction of fire ants from South America.

The Texas horned lizard has vanished from much of its former range in East Texas and is decreasing in the northern and central portions of the state. Southern and western populations seem to be more stable, but the Texas horned lizard and its close relatives need and deserve complete protection. Few creatures are more typically Texan than the official state reptile, the harmless and charming little "horny toad."

WHOOPING CRANE

Grus americana

Texas hosts no wildlife species more elegant than the tall and stately whooping crane. Indeed, the whooper is arguably one of the most famous birds in the world, and its fascinating story has been called "a love affair of two nations with a great white bird." At the present time, the only wild breeding flock of whooping cranes stages a phenomenal migration each year between its Canadian nesting grounds and its winter sanctuary along the Texas Coastal Bend.

The tallest bird in North America, the whooper once ranged over much of the continent. Although widespread, it was probably never abundant, and estimates of the population in 1870 range from 500 to 1,400 birds. These cranes rapidly gave way to the advance of human settlers across the land. Many were shot for food or trophies; others vanished as their marshlands were drained and cleared.

When President Franklin D. Roosevelt signed an executive order creating the federal Aransas Migratory Waterfowl Refuge on December 31, 1937, only two small flocks of whooping cranes remained. One flock migrated along the present route between Canada and Texas. The other remained year-round in Louisiana. The latter nonmigratory flock of a dozen cranes was halved by a tropical storm in 1940, and the remaining

Louisiana birds disappeared one by one within the next few years. The new Texas refuge, now known as the Aransas National Wildlife Refuge, provided a haven for all of the whooping cranes remaining in the wild. The fate of this magnificent bird rested on a tiny remnant of only fifteen individuals.

The nesting grounds of these migratory cranes went undiscovered until 1954. After several searches had failed, a forester and helicopter pilot flying to a wildfire spotted adults with young along the Sass River in Wood Buffalo National Park in the Northwest Territories. Since then, Canadian and U.S. biologists have been able to study the whooping cranes on their breeding grounds and to follow them on their annual migration of some 2,400 miles between this remote corner of northern Canada and the Texas coast.

Although whooping cranes lay two eggs, only one chick normally survives. Thus, at no risk to the nesting success of the wild population, the biologists began in 1967 to remove one egg from some of the nests in order to raise a captive flock at the Patuxent Research Center of the U.S. Fish and Wildlife Service in Laurel, Maryland. In 1975, encouraged by the results of these experiments, eggs were also placed in the nests of sandhill cranes at Idaho's Grays Lake National Wildlife Refuge. This practice continued for several years and seemed at first to have enormous potential. The fledgling whoopers migrated with their foster-parent sandhill cranes from Idaho to refuges in New Mexico, and hopes rose that they would form the nucleus of a new flock far removed from any dangers threatening their Texas relatives. Unfortunately, they apparently "never learned how to be whooping cranes" and showed no interest in mating with others of their kind as they reached adulthood. Many succumbed to accidents and predators, and the experiment was finally terminated. Efforts to establish a second flock have now shifted to Florida's Kissimmee Prairie, where chicks reared in isolation at the International Crane Foundation in Baraboo, Wisconsin, are being released.

The migratory flock wintering in Texas, meanwhile, has been slowly increasing due to added protection and concern. From a low of fifteen birds in 1941, the population passed 100 in 1986. Success has not come without occasional setbacks. In the fall of 1990, a record 146 whooping cranes arrived on the Texas coast from Canada, but only 134 survived to make the return journey. At least one was shot by a careless hunter. Others were killed by predators or died of other causes. Because of a severe drought the following summer, overall breeding success was also poor, and only nine new chicks survived the season. By the time the flock reached Aransas in 1991, it numbered 131 birds. Such declines seem to occur every ten years, although crane biologists can find no clear reason for the cyclic pattern. More recently, the population has spiraled upward once again. A total of 158 whooping cranes reached Texas in 1995, the highest number recorded in modern times. Only one chick failed to survive the winter.

The future of the whooping crane shines far more brightly now than it did a half-century ago, but the fate of the elegant birds is by no means assured. Constant efforts are necessary to limit coastal erosion and to protect the flock from potential oil or chemical spills in the Intracoastal Canal that traverses the Aransas Refuge. One of the busiest waterways in the world, the canal serves barges carrying a host of toxic materials that could quickly decimate the flock. As their numbers grow, the cranes also require more area in which to live.

The great white birds begin arriving at Aransas in late October and remain into April. Migrating in family groups, they return unerringly across the continent to their territories of previous years. There they defend an area of as much as a square mile of coastal marsh, where they stalk the shallows in search of food. Blue crabs constitute a major portion of their diet that also includes clams, small fish, acorns, berries, roots and grains. The long-legged cranes roost standing in shallow water, where it is more difficult for predators to approach. More than 75,000 visitors from around the world converge on the Texas coast each winter to see the state's most famous birds. Few experiences in nature equal a personal encounter with a family of whooping cranes.

The tall, regal birds stride across the coastal marsh, stopping occasionally to pluck tasty morsels from the shallow water. One of the adults catches a blue crab and drops it on the muddy bank, where the juvenile grabs it and wolfs it down. The parents are clad in immaculate white plumage. Their elongated tertial feathers form the "bustle" that gives all cranes their distinctive shape. Slightly smaller, the youngster is still washed and mottled with rusty brown.

The trio wanders a little farther and then launches into the air. Wings spanning seven feet beat ponderously, revealing for the first time the black wing tips that are hidden except in flight. Long necks are outstretched; legs trail far out behind. Across the marsh comes the trumpeting call, *ker-loo ker-lee-loo*, resonating within the coiled, five-foot-long windpipe of this giant bird. It is an echo from the Pleistocene, an indelible tableau drawn from one of conservation's greatest success stories.

Golden-Cheeked Warbler

Dendroica chrysoparia

The New World warblers have been called the "butterflies of the bird world" because of their brilliant colors, small size and constant activity. More than fifty species ornament the forests and fields of North America, and many of them occur in Texas, at least during certain seasons of the year. Some nest and raise their young within the boundaries of our state, while others arrive to spend the winter when chill winds sweep down across the North. Still more warblers move through Texas on their long migration flights, commuting between the northern breeding grounds and their winter refuges in tropical America, filling the trees with rainbow hues.

These tiny warblers rank among the most beautiful of all our birds, but few shine more brightly than the golden-cheeked warbler. The adult male, as its name implies, has a golden yellow face framed by a black crown, bib and back. A prominent black line extends through the eye, while the gleaming white underparts are also streaked with black along the sides. Females and immature birds wear a duller olive green above but are no less charming in their subdued plumage.

What makes the golden-cheeked warbler truly unique, however, is the fact that among all the warbler species, indeed among approximately 600 bird species that occur in Texas, only this one breeds entirely within the state's boundaries. Every golden-cheeked warbler in the world fledged from a nest on the Edwards Plateau of central Texas. This little feathered gem has one of the most restrictive nesting ranges of any North American bird.

In the mid-1970s, an estimated 7,500 pairs of warblers inhabited the Edwards Plateau and adjacent counties to the north. Now there may be no more than 1,500 pairs remaining, and this native Texan faces serious problems. On May 4, 1990, the U.S. Fish and Wildlife Service added the golden-cheeked warbler to its endangered species list on an emergency basis because of habitat loss. That temporary classification was later ratified under the Endangered Species Act and published in the *Federal Register* on December 27, 1990.

Golden-cheeks spend the winter in Central America and are very early migrants in both directions, their hazardous flights taking them across the Sierra Madre Oriental of Mexico. Males begin arriving in the Texas Hill Country in early March, to be followed by the females a few days later. The males' buzzy courtship songs, often described as *bzzzz layzee dayzee*, echo through the limestone hills and canyons, and the mated females soon select their nesting sites and begin to build.

As Warren Pulich notes in his book, *The Golden-cheeked Warbler*, the species is obligate on Ashe juniper. Somewhere along its evolutionary path, this little warbler acquired the compulsive need to construct nests of

©-Gamini Ratnavira

strips of bark from mature Ashe juniper trees. The female pulls the long strips from the tree and weaves them into a little cup, binding them with spider webs. She then lines the nest with grasses, feathers and fur, providing a soft bed for her four speckled eggs.

Neither the bark from young trees nor that from any other species of juniper, locally called "cedar," seems to be acceptable to the golden-cheeked warbler, and the species is thus confined to habitats in which Ashe juniper predominates. It represents an amazing dependence on a single environmental niche, a dependence that spells trouble for the lovely little bird as its habitat disappears.

Stands of Ashe juniper alone, however, do not constitute prime warbler habitat. Indeed, although the bark is required for construction, two-thirds of the nests are actually placed in oaks and other deciduous trees. Because the birds are totally insectivorous, they also depend on a diversity of trees, shrubs, grasses and wildflowers to provide the numerous caterpillars and other insects they require for themselves and for their young. Oaks harbor many more insects than do junipers, probably because of toxic terpenes in juniper foliage.

Only on Texas' Edwards Plateau does Ashe juniper grow with the several species of oaks, redbud, bumelia, cedar elm, pecan, river walnut and other such trees that support the requisite insect populations. Nesting golden-cheeks have been observed in at least ten Hill Country state parks as well as on the surrounding private land. Lost Maples State Natural Area is home to an estimated 100 pairs and remains the easiest public place to see these rare birds, particularly in March and April when courting males sing loudly from the tops of the trees. Pedernales Falls, Colorado Bend, Guadalupe River, Garner, Kerrville, Longhorn Caverns, Meridian and Dinosaur Valley State Parks also harbor golden-cheeked warblers.

Brood parasitism by the brown-headed cowbird is often cited as a major factor in the decline of the golden-cheeked warbler; however, recent research by Mark Lockwood of the Texas Parks & Wildlife Department indicates the effects may be smaller than expected. Because the warblers nest so early in the spring, their breeding season precedes that of most cowbirds. If the first warbler nest is destroyed, however, subsequent attempts are more subject to parasitism. Even then, Lockwood suggests, cowbirds pose a far more serious threat to the similarly endangered black-capped vireo than to the golden-cheeked warbler.

Habitat fragmentation; urban expansion and development; overgrazing by cattle, sheep and goats; and clearing of the land for other uses threaten a large portion of the golden-cheek's range. A recent survey reported a loss of up to 45 percent of the suitable habitat over a ten-year period. Satellite imagery indicates that of approximately 57,000 acres remaining, 70 percent is in fragments too small for the birds to use.

Habitat preservation constitutes the single most important concern in the fight to preserve the only bird we can consider a pure-bred Texan. And, in saving that vital environment, we provide not only for the colorful and charming golden-cheeked warbler but for a host of other Texas plants and animals as well.

BARTON SPRINGS SALAMANDER

Eurycea sosorum

Barton Springs in Austin's Zilker Park has served as a popular swimming hole and local gathering place for more than seventy years. Bathers share the waters with various forms of aquatic life, and therein lies an ongoing controversy. One of the residents, the rare Barton Springs salamander, lives nowhere else.

A recent survey found 188 of the tiny salamanders within the spring complex. Although this is a record number, it is a very small population on which to base the future of an entire species. The fate of this two-and-a-half-inch amphibian depends on maintaining the flow and purity of water from the springs.

In 1994, the U.S. Fish and Wildlife Service proposed listing the Barton Springs salamander as "endangered" under the provisions of the Endangered Species Act. While environmentalists heralded the proposal, local landowners and developers were vehemently opposed, fearing it would lead to restrictions on development in the surrounding area that feeds the aquifer.

There were several threats to the salamander, the government report concluded. Contamination of the waters that drain into the Barton Springs complex would be disastrous, and because of the small area involved, a single incident could impact an entire species. Reduction of the ground

Texas blind salamander

water and disturbance of the Barton Springs pool by cleaning with chemicals and high-pressure hoses could also prove detrimental. To further evaluate the status of the salamander, the Texas Parks and Wildlife Department (TPWD) assembled a scientific team made up of biologists, an ecologist, a geohydrologist and an engineer. Most were from outside Texas, thereby ensuring objectivity. It was, the state agency noted, its first effort to develop an independent peer-review process for issues such as endangered species listing.

The team also concluded that chemical spills and sedimentation posed the greatest threats, and four government agencies combined to develop a conservation plan for the Barton Springs salamander. The plan was heralded as "a national standard for innovative wildlife conservation." The actions proposed would "accomplish every objective that might have resulted from a federal listing," said Dr. Larry McKinney, TPWD senior division director for water policy. "It will ensure that this remarkable spring ecosystem will continue to be enjoyed by future generations, and it shows how Texans are taking care of Texas through good cooperation between landowners, government agencies, and others."

Under the plan, TPWD was charged with setting up a captive-breeding program to avoid extinction of the salamander in case the natural population suffered a major disaster. The department was also to assist the city of Austin in establishing pool maintenance procedures.

Then, in December, 1996, twelve salamanders were found dead after a routine draining and cleaning of the Barton Springs pool. Another cleaning in January, 1997, killed sixteen more, and state and federal wildlife agencies asked the city to suspend the weekly cleanings. By decreasing the water level, the spring outlets had been allowed to dry up, leaving the aquatic salamanders high and dry to perish in the sun.

The controversy is far from over. The federal government has again proposed listing the Barton Springs salamander as endangered, and Texas politicians protest that they have been betrayed. Lost in the heated debate is the fact that both the citizens of Texas and the salamanders benefit from the preservation of water quality in Barton Springs. Amphibians serve as sensitive indicators of our environment, and their loss presages potential problems for everyone.

The Barton Springs salamander is by no means the only one that faces possible extinction in the scenic Hill Country of central Texas. The Texas blind salamander inhabits subterranean streams and caves of the Edwards Aquifer near San Marcos. Because it lives in perpetual darkness, it lacks functional eyes, and its skin is a ghostly white or pale pink. This extremely rare and unusual amphibian has occupied a place on the federal endangered-species list since 1967.

Occurring nearby is the San Marcos salamander, an inhabitant of Spring Lake and the adjacent downstream portion of the San Marcos River. There it lives among the aquatic mosses and algae growing in the pools, feeding on small invertebrates and seeking shelter among the boulders and beneath the vegetation. It is classified as "threatened" on both federal and state lists.

Also limited to similar environmental niches in the Edwards Aquifer are two tiny fish, the San Marcos gambusia and the fountain darter. They, too, are considered "endangered" and with the salamanders depend on clean, clear, flowing water for their existence. As population growth and the increased use of groundwater lead to decreasing spring flow, all face an uncertain future.

Texas' Cascade Caverns salamander has been found only in the subterranean waters of Cascade Caverns in Kendall County, while the Comal blind salamander lives in Honey Creek Cave and nearby sinkholes of Comal County and in Elm Springs Cave in Bexar County. The Blanco blind salamander is confined to underground streams and caves north and east of the Blanco River.

All of these rare creatures are confined to small environmental niches in Texas, and all have been placed on the state's list of threatened and endangered species. Each depends on a continued supply of clean, clear water, but in that requirement they differ little from other wildlife around the globe.

Management guidelines for the preservation of the Edwards Aquifer salamanders and fish call for the following measures: (1) conserve water; (2) prevent water pollution; (3) prevent damage to streambed vegetation and bottom substrates; (4) manage surface vegetation to prevent erosion and runoff; (5) avoid introduction of non-native plants and animals. It is a prescription that would benefit us all.

Black-Capped Vireo

Vireo atricapillus

The Texas checklist presently contains thirteen species of vireos, although three are listed as "accidental" and seldom cross the state borders. Some, like the white-eyed and red-eyed vireos, occur widely across eastern Texas, while such western species as Hutton's vireo and the gray vireo are confined to small areas of the Trans-Pecos. They resemble warblers in size, ranging from about four to six inches in length, but have chunkier profiles and heavier bills with slightly hooked tips. Less active than warblers, which normally flit quickly through the treetops, vireos feed by methodically gleaning insects from the undersides of the leaves. Many sing incessantly through the day, even at noon when most other birds lapse into quiet lethargy.

Unlike the brightly colored warblers, most vireos wear somber shades of olive green and gray. In fact, the name *vireo* comes from the Latin *virere*, "to be green." Some species have prominent light wing bars and bright eye-rings linked to form "spectacles." The others lack the wing bars and spectacles but have pronounced eyebrow stripes.

The smallest of all North American vireos, the black-capped vireo is also the most strikingly marked. Olive above and white below, the male has yellowish flanks and bright yellow wing bars. He also wears a dapper, distinctive black helmet and conspicuous white spectacles, while the drabber female has a slate gray cap and whitish wing bars. Scarcely larger than a kinglet, the black-capped vireo flits about more quickly than other members of its genus, gleaning caterpillars and beetles from the foliage, often hanging head downward in a characteristic pose before fluttering to a lower branch.

The nesting range of the black-capped vireo formerly extended from central Kansas through Oklahoma and Texas into Mexico. It prefers rocky canyons and low ridges with bright sunlight, locations that one ornithologist described as "the hottest places imaginable." There its restless and remarkably varied song could be heard throughout the breeding season. Unfortunately, that song has been stilled in portions of the species' former range. The black-capped vireo was last reported in Kansas in 1953, and recent census work in Oklahoma showed there to be no more than thirty to fifty breeding pairs in that state.

Once locally common in the oak-juniper thickets of central and western Texas, the vireo has vanished from much of that range as well. Its major stronghold remains on the Edwards Plateau, an environmental niche it shares with the golden-cheeked warbler, another bird presently included on the federal list of endangered species. The black-capped vireo attained that dubious distinction in October of 1987.

At least eight state parks presently harbor populations of this rare vireo, with Devil's River State Natural Area and Kickapoo Cavern State Park hosting an estimated 190

and 140 pairs, respectively. About 300 pairs also find a home on the grounds of Fort Hood, where they are well protected from intruders. Over most of its range, however, one of Texas' most distinctive birds faces possible extinction because of severe habitat loss due to urban sprawl and real-estate development. Brood parasitism by the brown-headed cowbird also poses a very real threat.

Arriving in early spring from their wintering grounds in the Pacific foothills of western Mexico, black-capped vireos prefer to nest in habitats where thickets of low trees combine with heavy ground cover. Unlike golden-cheeked warblers, which insist on using Ashe juniper bark to build their nests, the vireos have no obligation to any particular plant species. They utilize many different shrubs and small trees, but appear partial to those that are unpalatable to cattle, an obvious advantage on grazing land. According to Texas Parks & Wildlife biologist Mark Lockwood, Texas persimmon, agarita and evergreen sumac provide favorite sites.

The compact, cuplike nest of plant fibers and bark strips hangs in a fork or between two low branches and is usually well concealed. Both sexes share in the nest building and incubating their three to five white eggs, which hatch in about fourteen days. The young fledge nine to eleven days later. On leaving the nest, the family is split, each parent caring for a portion of the hungry brood.

Vireos nesting on the southern portion of the Edwards Plateau may start in March, well before the normal reproductive cycle of the cowbirds, and successfully hatch their eggs and raise their young without interference. Later nesters and those that attempt to raise a second brood, however, face severe problems from the parasitic cowbirds. Indeed, studies in some areas have documented parasitism in up to 90 percent of the vireo nests.

Dropping in on an untended nest, the female cowbird frequently removes one of the host's eggs before depositing her own. Even when eggs of both species are incubated by the unwitting "foster parents," the odds are stacked heavily in favor of the young cowbirds. They hatch more quickly than the vireos, and even if the adults persist until their own eggs hatch, the nearly helpless vireo chicks are poorly matched in competition with the older and larger interlopers for nest space and food. Seldom do the vireos succeed in raising their own young in company with cowbirds.

According to Lockwood's surveys, the Texas population of black-capped vireos is fairly stable, as is the one in Coahuila, Mexico. However, a cowbird-eradication program has been considered to further the interests of both the vireo and the golden-cheeked warbler. "There doesn't seem to be any other way," said Bob Short of the U.S. Fish and Wildlife Service. "The cowbird is such a problem for reproduction that the vireo might not have a chance." The Service also cites habitat loss due to urbanization, range management, overbrowsing by animals, and the change in plant succession as critical factors in the decline of one of the Texas Hill Country's characteristic and most fascinating birds.

Endangered Plants

Lloyd's hedgehog cactus

Few other states can equal Texas' plant diversity. From the lush East Texas forests to the arid deserts of the Trans-Pecos, and from the rolling Panhandle plains to the subtropical thorn-scrub woodlands of the lower Rio Grande Valley, Texas provides an enormous range of geological landforms, soils and climates. With that range of conditions goes an attendant variety of floral communities and a phenomenal total of nearly 6,000 native plants.

Best known of Texas wildflowers, perhaps, are those that bloom profusely along the highways in early spring. Bluebonnets, Indian paintbrush, evening-primrose and many others put on an incredible display, luring tens of thousands of people onto the "bluebonnet trails," "dogwood trails" and other widely publicized routes winding across the state. Various other floral species provide a continuing spectacle throughout the seasons of the year.

Not all native plants grow in such abundance, however, and botanists estimate that 10 percent of all Texas species should be considered rare or uncommon because of their highly specialized habitats or limited numbers. Perhaps as many as 200 are in jeopardy of disappearing entirely from our botanical legacy.

Texas wild-rice

The Convention on International Trade in Endangered Species (CITES) lists worldwide plants and animals in danger of extinction and seeks to protect them on a global scale. Within the state, the Texas Natural Heritage Program of the Texas Parks and Wildlife Department and the Texas Organization for Endangered Species (TOES) have compiled lists of threatened and endangered plants. The U.S. Endangered Species Act of 1973 provides for federal protection of plants as well as animals, while Texas passed legislation in 1981 adding plant conservation to the Texas Parks and Wildlife Code.

Texas wild-rice (*Zizania texana*) became the first plant from our state to be classified as federally endangered. One of thirteen plant species from around the country that were listed in an April, 1978, decision, it is found only in the upper reaches of the San Marcos River. Increasing use of the river for recreation and the introduction of alien plants had caused a severe decline, and the remaining population had not produced seeds in many years. Without protection under the Endangered Species Act, it was surely destined for extinction. One of only two species of wild-rice that occur in the United States, this warm-weather form could prove useful in hybridization with the commercial wild-rice that grows farther north.

In 1980, the first cacti were added to the endangered species list. Twenty-one species from the southwestern states were named, including Texas' Nellie cory cactus (*Coryphantha minima)*, Davis' green pitaya (*Echinocereus viridiflorus var. davisii)*, Sneed pincushion cactus (*Coryphantha sneedii var. sneedii)*, and the bunched cory cactus (*Coryphantha ramillosa)*. All grow in arid regions of the Trans-Pecos, sharing those desert gravels and rugged, rocky mountain slopes with the Chisos hedgehog cactus (*Echinocereus chisoenis var. chisoensis)*, Lloyd's hedgehog cactus (*Echinocereus lloydii),* and Lloyd's mariposa cactus (*Neolloydia mari-*

posensis). Each is now classified as threatened or endangered, and each depends on small relict populations.

Collecting poses the greatest threat. Although all of these cacti are small, they put on large, colorful blooms in season, and they are highly prized by plant collectors. Indeed, cactus rustlers and smugglers have dug up

Black lace cactus

enormous numbers of some of the rarest species, funneling them into the lucrative interstate and foreign black-market trade.

The rare black lace cactus (*Echinocereus reichenbachii var. albertii)* grows not in West Texas with the other endangered cacti but along the Gulf Coastal Plain in Jim Wells, Kleberg and Refugio Counties. Its small stems sheathed with lacy white spines tipped with purple and its three-inch rose-purple flowers make it another popular plant for collectors. The major threat, however, lies in the continuing conversion of the brushy grasslands in which it lives to more profitable pasture and agricultural fields.

Texas' vanishing plants range from the dwarf, four-foot Hinckley's oak (*Quercus hinckleyi)* that inhabits the Chihuahuan scrub in Presidio County to the Navasota ladies'-tresses (*Spiranthes parksii*) along the tributaries of the Brazos and Navasota Rivers in the eastern portions of the state. The oak, known to grow in three small populations of fewer than sixty plants each, is threatened by overgrazing and road construction; the lovely little orchid faces ever-increasing land development.

To lose a species forever is cause enough for alarm. However, we know so little about many of these plants that we cannot begin to estimate their true value.

Botanists point out that the seeds of white bladderpod (*Lesquerella pallida)*, which grows only in alkaline seeps amid East Texas pines, may contain a high-quality oil of

Hinckley's oak

Navasota ladies'-tresses

potential value. McKittrick pennyroyal (*Hedeoma apiculatum)* probably has medicinal uses as do many other members of its genus, and the endangered ashy dogweed (*Thymophylla tephroleuca)*, known from only one location in South Texas, has leaves filled with aromatic compounds that could prove useful for a variety of human needs.

Prairie dawn (*Hymenoxys texana),* also called Texas bitterweed, can now be found only in Harris and Fort Bend Counties, where it inhabits poorly drained saline depressions around small, sandy mounds. Its remaining habitat is disappearing rapidly in the face of urban sprawl. A tiny plant without large blooms, it nevertheless has interesting genetic components that enable it to thrive in soils unsuited for most other plants.

Texas snowbells (*Styrax texana)* of the Edwards Plateau is a small, slender shrub with lovely white flowers that deserves a wider audience. Also worthy of future cultivation are Texas poppy-mallow (*Callirhoe scabriuscula*) with its magenta flowers, Texas trailing phlox (*Phlox nivalis ssp. texensis)*, and large-fruited sand verbena (*Abronia macrocarpa)*.

Taking the national lead in plant preservation is the Center for Plant Conservation headquartered at the Missouri Botanical Garden in St. Louis. Founded in 1984, the CPC hopes to conserve native plant species by maintaining collections of stored seeds and living plants within more than a

Prairie dawn

Texas trailing phlox

score of participating institutions across the country. Harris County's Mercer Arboretum and Botanic Gardens and the San Antonio Botanical Center are the two member facilities in Texas. Each maintains gardens of locally threatened species, and each is concerned with their preservation and propagation.

CPC estimates place the number of U.S. plants at significant risk of extinction at 4,400 species, roughly one-fifth of our nation's native flora. Eight hundred may vanish within the decade without intervention. Texas is home to more than a hundred of those severely threatened species, and they constitute a botanical treasure-trove we cannot afford to lose.

Texas poppy-mallow

White bladderpod

Large-fruited sand verbena

Texas snowbells

Comanche Springs Pupfish

Cyprinodon elegans

Pecos Gambusia

Gambusia nobilis

Fed by the flow from a desert spring, the tiny stream sparkles in the bright sunlight of an early-summer afternoon. Away to the southwest, the ancient, weathered peaks of the Davis Mountains loom on the horizon. Curve-billed thrashers and Inca doves feed along the stream banks, while scaled quail parade through the desert scrub. From a nearby cottonwood, a sleek black phoebe darts down to snatch an insect from the surface of the water and returns to the shelter of its shady perch. As the heat builds, the birds fall silent. Only an occasional lizard scurries across the searing sand.

The trickling stream, however, teems with life, even under the midday sun. Silvery Mexican tetras and green sunfish swim back and forth among aquatic plants. A blotched water snake emerges cautiously from its den, forked tongue flicking rapidly in and out to test the air.

Small, chunky Comanche Springs pupfish, each no more than two inches long, swirl about in the shallow water. Dominant

Pecos gambusia

males aggressively defend their territories, darting out to repel rival males, sidling up to prospective mates in ardent invitation. Flushed with hormonal color, the males glisten with a metallic blue sheen, a dark band tipping their rounded, whitish tails. Darker blotches mark the gray-green females, the spots merging into a broken stripe along the paler sides.

Comanche Springs pupfish

Once a female accepts her suitor's attentions, the two swim round and round in piscatorial fervor, the male curling his tail about his chosen mate. Small jets of milky spawn mark the union; fertilized eggs drop into a shallow depression scooped in the bottom sediments. All along the little stream other pupfish are similarly occupied, completely oblivious to everything except the instinctive urge to reproduce.

Pecos gambusia also make their home in this outflow from the spring, sharing their habitat with the pupfish. Slender, inch-long males swim beside heavier-bodied, two-inch females in a frenzied water ballet, much in the manner of courting guppies in a home aquarium. Some of the females are as yet unmated; others are already swollen with young soon to be born alive.

Similar scenes may occur in streams across the continent, but this particular tableau is unique. Both the Comanche Springs pupfish and the Pecos gambusia are listed as federally endangered and rank among the rarest fishes in Texas. The matings serve to perpetuate two species that occur only in desert springs welling up from deep beneath the sand and rock of Trans-Pecos Texas. Most reside in a carefully maintained habitat in Balmorhea State Park.

This small park is best known for the world's largest spring-fed swimming pool. Summer bathers enjoy its constant temperature of 72° to 76° F, and land-locked scuba divers practice in its twenty-five-foot depths. The waters of San Solomon Springs feed the one-and-three-fourths-acre pool, and the runoff trickles down through a series of channels to a man-made but biologically functional cienega, or desert marsh. This newly completed refuge creates a place not only for the pupfish and gambusia but for a variety of other native plants and animals as well.

Dependent on the constant temperature and fresh water of such springs, the Comanche Springs pupfish historically occurred only in the Balmorhea system and in Comanche Springs in Fort Stockton. The latter went dry in 1955, however, and its fragile namesake occupants were gone.

Similarly, the Pecos gambusia disappeared from Comanche Springs and from Leon Springs, which suffered a similar fate. It now survives in the San Solomon waters and in the outflow from Diamond-Y Spring north of Fort Stockton. Limited numbers also occur northward into New Mexico.

These two rare desert fish are not the only ones that face an uncertain future. The Big Bend gambusia now lives only in spring-fed pools near Boquillas Crossing and Rio Grande Village in Big Bend National Park. Decimated when Boquillas Spring ceased to flow and when other populations were lost to a fishing pond for the campground, all of the present survivors are descended from a tiny remnant of two males and one female captured in 1956.

Habitat loss from declining spring flow constitutes the most immediate threat to many of the desert fish. More groundwater is removed by pumping for irrigation and other human uses than can be replaced by the meager rainfall across this arid land. The result is the drying up of the springs and the loss of their inhabitants.

Competition and hybridization with introduced species also threaten native populations. The Big Bend gambusia, for example, suffers in competition with the western mosquitofish that shares its few remaining pools.

Few ecological niches are more fragile than these verdant springs and the drainages they feed. Many harbor plants and animals found nowhere else. Now protected by the Texas Nature Conservancy, Diamond-Y Spring is one of the last refuges not only for the Pecos gambusia but for the Leon Springs pupfish, *Cyprinodon bovinus*. First discovered in Leon Springs in 1851, that little pupfish was thought to be extinct when the spring dried up. Then, in 1965, it was rediscovered in Diamond-Y, where it presently occupies two three-mile, spring-fed segments of Diamond-Y Draw and Leon Creek into which it flows. Here, too, biologists have found two different species of rare, endemic snails and the threatened puzzle sunflower.

The waters of San Solomon, Diamond-Y and other such fragile desert springs contain an array of species that occur nowhere else on earth. Other nearby springs have already ceased to flow, and those that remain grasp tenuously at life. Each feeds an oasis of life-forms unique to the deserts of Trans-Pecos Texas. Each is a treasure of enormous worth.

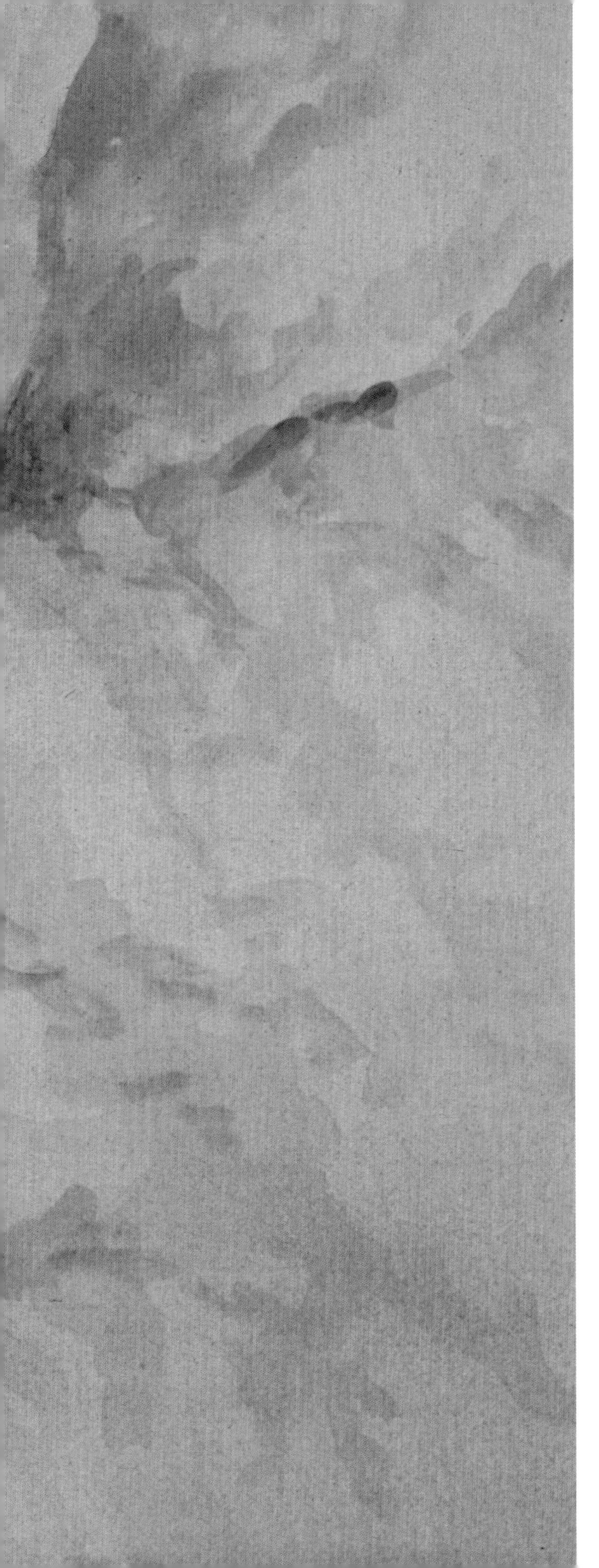

Aplomado Falcon

Falco femoralis

The elegant and superbly graceful aplomado falcon once ranged widely throughout the open grasslands and deserts of the American Southwest, from the tidal flats and coastal prairies of southern Texas across New Mexico to Arizona. Early naturalists described it as "fairly common" along the Rio Grande, and some biologists suggest it may have outnumbered the white-tailed hawk and crested caracara that shared its habitat.

The latter two birds of prey remain throughout South Texas to the present day, but the aplomado falcon began to decline by the beginning of the twentieth century and ultimately vanished from the U.S. and northern Mexico. Now, however, a concerted program of captive breeding and release promises to restore this beautiful raptor to its former range.

The name *aplomado* comes from the Spanish word for "lead-colored," reflecting the bird's dark, slate gray back and upper wing surfaces. Smaller than the peregrine and prairie falcons, but larger than the merlin and kestrel, the aplomado falcon has long, slender, pointed wings and a long, banded tail. Its upper breast and throat are white or buff; its lower belly and thighs are bright cinnamon. Dark patches on the sides often extend across the breast in a dapper and distinctive cummerbund. The boldly marked head pattern is also diagnostic, with the dark "mustache" marks characteristic of falcons and pale eyebrows that meet behind the head.

The original range of the northern aplomado falcon, *Falco femoralis septentrionalis*, extended from the southern U.S. borderlands through Mexico and Guatemala. Other races occur sparingly southward from Panama across much of South America to Tierra del Fuego.

Although little is known of this rare falcon's social behavior, pairs usually remain together throughout the year and select abandoned twig nests of other hawks and ravens in which to lay their clutch of two or three eggs.

Adults hunt cooperatively within their nesting territory. According to some accounts, the male searches more widely for prey and then calls his mate to join in the pursuit. The streamlined birds fly swiftly and low to the ground, and are capable of overtaking fleeing birds with amazing bursts of speed. Doves, killdeer, grackles and other small birds make up a major portion of their diet, while rodents, insects and occasional snakes and lizards supplement this avian fare. The falcons also land to pursue, on foot, prey that scrambles through the treetops or tries futilely to escape by hiding among the grasses or beneath scattered shrubs.

The last recorded breeding of native aplomado falcons in Texas occurred in 1941, when a nest with three eggs was observed north of Edinburg in Brooks County. Occasional nests were then reported in New Mexico until 1952, after which the species was apparently extirpated from the United States. Vagrant birds appeared at rare intervals in Big Bend National Park and Trans-Pecos Texas and on the southern Gulf Coast, but no more nesting attempts were detected. The northern aplomado falcon was placed on the federal list of endangered species in February, 1986.

The reasons for its demise remain uncertain. Most sources list habitat loss and pesticides as the main contributors, but Oberholser, in his epic *The Bird Life of Texas*, notes that the decline began long before the widespread use of DDT and other persistent pesticides.

Indeed, many factors probably came into play. Some birds were killed by random shooting, while the brown-spotted white eggs proved popular with egg collectors, a practice now illegal under modern wildlife laws. Overgrazing and conversion of grasslands to agricultural fields undoubtedly played a role, as did the loss of riparian woodlands along desert streams. These land-use changes were accompanied by a dramatic decline of prey species on which the raptors fed. Invasion of mesquite and other brush on the prairies also caused aplomado falcons to desert their established territories, probably because the birds found it more difficult to hunt in denser cover. All these factors doubtless contributed to a downward spiral. The subsequent pesticide contamination that thinned egg shells and caused breeding failures did not allow the colorful falcons to recolonize their former range. One of our most magnificent birds of prey seemed lost forever.

Then, in 1984, The Peregrine Fund, Inc., a nonprofit organization dedicated to the preservation of world-wide species, began research on the rearing and release of the aplomado falcon. The first captive breeding of the species at Texas' Chihuahuan Desert Research Institute and subsequent studies by the Santa Cruz, California, Predatory Bird Research Group hinted at potential success, but an enormous effort would be required.

With twenty-five baby falcons obtained from remnant populations in Mexico, The Peregrine Fund succeeded in establishing more than thirty pairs of aplomados in their breeding program at the World Center for Birds of Prey in Boise, Idaho. Downy chicks hatched in captivity were then transported to Laguna Atascosa National Wildlife Refuge on the lower Texas coast and placed in "hack boxes" atop elevated platforms, where they could be fed and cared for until ready to fledge and hunt on their own.

There were no guarantees of success, for biologists estimate that 70 percent of young falcons cannot catch enough prey to survive their first year, and great horned owls and other large predators take a heavy toll. Nevertheless, excited visitors to Laguna Atascosa Refuge could occasionally see aplomado falcons flying free over the coastal marshes and prairies. The program continues to the present day, with more than 100 falcons released at Laguna Atascosa and additional birds sent to Matagorda Island farther up the coast.

It was in May, 1995, that the excitement reached fever pitch. Unexpectedly, a pair of falcons established a nest atop a sixty-five-foot utility pole on a remote tract of grassland and salt flats owned by the Port of Brownsville. There they fledged a single chick, the first known successful wild nesting of the aplomado falcon in the United States in forty-three years.

This landmark moment represents only the first step, but hope burns brightly that one of our most beautiful and elegant birds of prey has returned to Texas from the brink of extinction.

Brown Pelican

Pelecanus occidentalis

Two species of pelicans occur in Texas and across the United States, the brown pelican and the larger white pelican. The wings of the former span seven feet; those of the latter, an astounding nine feet. Early settlers who sailed to our coast frequently wrote of seeing thousands of white and brown pelicans perched on the shores of aptly named Pelican Island in Galveston Bay. William Gray, visiting the area in 1836, noted the birds "at a distance resembled companies of soldiers, white and gray; the two colors flock together."

In spite of their many similarities, the two species have very different methods of feeding. Brown pelicans dive headlong into the water from high in the air, entering beak first and sometimes disappearing from sight beneath the waves. White pelicans do not dive. Instead, they float buoyantly on the water and scoop up fish with their dip-net bills.

The bill of a pelican is several times as long as its head and ends in a clawlike hook. On the underside are long extensions of the lower jawbones that join only at the tip and can be spread widely. Between these bones hangs the pouch, which can contract when not in use or expand to serve as a net. After scooping up its catch, the pelican closes and raises its bill, contracts the pouch to force out the water and swallows the fish.

It was once believed that pelicans carried home live fish in their pouches to feed their young. Actually, the chicks are fed a half-digested soup that their parents regurgitate and drip into their gaping mouths. Older chicks pursue this mixture by poking their heads deep into the throats of the adults in what ornithologist Terence Shortt described as "like a wrestling match, and the writhing and contorting are both alarming and revolting."

So bizarre are the massive beaks of both species that one can scarcely meet a pelican face to face without recalling Dixon Merritt's 1910 classic: "A wonderful bird is the pelican / His bill will hold more than his belican." This is not poetic license, for the pouch of the white pelican holds three gallons, more than twice the capacity of its stomach, and the pouch of the smaller brown pelican holds up to a gallon.

To regard either pelican as only a comic character, however, does it a grave disservice. Both are marvelously adapted for the special ecological niches they occupy. Although pelicans may look ludicrous waddling about on land, they are wonderfully graceful in flight. Heads pulled back to rest on their shoulders, they alternately flap and sail, with some of the slowest wingbeats of any bird. They travel in orderly lines and V-formations, flapping and sailing in rhythm, each picking up the beat from the bird ahead.

The pelican is widely represented in folklore, literature and art. During medieval times it became a symbol for Christ because of the erroneous belief that it picked at its breast until it bled in order to feed the blood to its nestlings. Ulisse Aldrovandi's multivolume ornithological treatise, published in Italy about 1600, included an engraving of just such a mythical scene. The Spanish name for the pelican, *alcatraz*, has also become a familiar part of our lexicon. The island in San Francisco Bay was named for the brown pelicans that inhabited it long before "The Rock" served as a prison.

An estimated 5,000 brown pelicans nested along the Texas coast in 1920. In the 1950s, however, observers noted a disastrous decline. Fewer and fewer adults were present, and nesting nearly ceased. This downward spiral continued until no young fledged between 1964 and 1966. An extensive survey in 1969 counted only 116 brown pelicans along the entire Texas coast, with none at all on Galveston Bay and the upper coast, where once they had been so plentiful.

In 1969, too, came word of trouble in the pelican colonies of California. Broken eggs littered the ground, their shells too thin to withstand the weight of incubating birds. It was a disaster presaged by Rachel Carson's 1962 classic, *Silent Spring*. The decline was apparently due to the gradual buildup of DDT and other chlorinated hydrocarbons in the environment and the birds' food chains. Sprayed on the land in massive amounts, the pesticides and their toxic residues washed into streams and down to the sea, where they were absorbed by marine micro-organisms. These were eaten by fish, and the fish, in turn, were consumed by the pelicans. Each successive step further concentrated the dangerous chemicals in the organs and fatty tissues of the hosts.

Concentrations were rarely enough to kill the giant birds outright, but they were sufficient to upset body chemistry and produce infertile or thin-shelled eggs. Brown pelicans were not the only victims of this inadvertent poisoning. Bald eagles, ospreys and peregrine falcons all suffered a similar decline, and all were eventually placed on the federal endangered-species list. The brown pelican officially achieved that dubious distinction throughout Texas, Louisiana and California in October, 1970.

White pelicans, on the other hand, fared better than their smaller cousins. Because they move inland during the breeding season, nesting on lakes and ponds across the western half of North America, and return to coastal waters only for the winter, they feed in a variety of habitats and, therefore, did not accumulate the same levels of pesticides.

Although there have also been sporadic breeding records for white pelicans along the Texas coast, in recent years the state has had only a single nesting colony on an island in the Laguna Madre in Kleberg County. Amazingly, this adjunct population is 1,400 miles from its nearest neighbors in Utah. Other white pelicans seen during the summer in Texas appear to be nonbreeding birds that do not bother to migrate northward. Instead, they wait patiently for the others to rejoin them in the fall.

DDT was banned for most uses in the United States in 1972, and bird populations began to recover quickly. Brown pelicans have returned to Texas in significant numbers, with hundreds now breeding again in Galveston Bay and southward along the Gulf Coast. The threat is by no means over, for chlorinated hydrocarbons are still in use in other countries, and they can spread insidiously down the rivers and through the oceans of the world. But at least for now, brown pelicans once again fly majestically over Texas shores.

Few scenes are more magnificent than day's end along the coast. The sky turns pink and orange with the glow of sunset and the water darkens to purple, its mirror surface broken only by the wake of a passing shrimp boat. Behind the boat flies a cloud of wheeling, screaming gulls, following it between the jetties and up the channel. Low over the water, a line of much larger brown pelicans flies slowly by in precise formation, huge dark birds with long, massive bills resting on their breasts.

Some are entirely gray-brown with lighter bellies, immature pelicans that will not attain adult plumage until their third year. Each adult in the formation is more handsomely attired, with blackish belly and white head and neck washed sparingly with yellow. In breeding plumage, the back of the neck turns deep chestnut, and the bill and facial skin flush with hormonal color.

Alternating between ponderous, flapping flight and short, arrow-straight glides, the birds skim the surface of the water. It seems impossible they can remain airborne with so little apparent effort. Massive size and majestic manner set pelicans apart from all other birdlife in the bay. Their distinctive profiles make them immediately recognizable, even in silhouette against the darkening sky.

Concho Water Snake

Nerodia harteri paucimaculata

Brazos Water Snake

Nerodia harteri harteri

Early in this century, a Minnesota native named Philip "Snakey" Harter moved to Texas and settled in Palo Pinto County. There he earned a living collecting reptiles and selling them to zoos, universities and other herpetologists until his death at the age of eighty-four. In 1938, a shipment sent to the Cornell University Museum contained a strange snake no one had ever seen before. It was first classified as a widespread and highly variable species that encompasses the yellowbelly and blotched water snakes. A second shipment in 1940, however, contained an identical specimen, and curiosity mounted.

Such snakes were common in little rocky riffles along the upper reaches of the Brazos River drainage, Harter responded, and he sent yet another shipment containing twenty live specimens. The result was the scientific description of a new species, Harter's water snake, *Nerodia harteri*. It is the only snake endemic to the state of Texas and thus found nowhere else throughout the world.

More recently, two different subspecies have been recognized. The one discovered by Snakey Harter is called the Brazos water snake, *Nerodia harteri harteri*. The other, first described in 1961, has been designated the Concho water snake,

Nerodia harteri paucimaculata. Both inhabit rocky, free-flowing streams, and the two subspecies are separated by miles of arid rangeland across north-central Texas.

Both are also threatened by changes to their habitats as dams and other water projects inundate the rocky river courses or alter the flow of tributaries. The Brazos water snake now occupies a place on the Texas list of threatened species. The Concho water snake was listed as "endangered" by the state in 1977 and officially placed on the federal list as "threatened" on September 3, 1986.

Relatively small compared to most other water snakes, the Concho and Brazos subspecies rarely reach a length of three feet, and most are considerably shorter. They are nonvenomous and completely harmless, although they may bite if handled carelessly.

The reddish or grayish brown body of the Concho water snake is marked with a checkerboard pattern created by four rows of alternating dark brown blotches, two on each side. It has lighter dorsal blotches than its Brazos River counterpart, and its light pinkish or orange underparts usually lack the characteristic dark spots at the ends of the belly scales. Hence its scientific epithet, *paucimaculata*, which means "fewer-spotted."

The Concho water snake was first collected from the South Concho River and Dove Creek west of San Angelo and historically occurred over 276 river miles of the Colorado and Concho drainages in central Texas. That range may once have been even larger, but the E. V. Spence Reservoir upstream and Lake Buchanan downstream have inundated many miles of appropriate habitat.

Optimal conditions consist of free-flowing streams that trickle over limestone bedrock or loose, tumbled stones. Quiet pools overflow, and the water trickles down through little riffles to other pools below. Periodic floods scour the riverbed, removing muddy sediments that build up between the rocks and clearing the banks and bars of encroaching underbrush.

The snakes hibernate in the numerous cracks and crevices among the rocks through the winter months and find shelter during the intense midsummer heat. They are active from March through October, but forage mainly in the early morning and evening hours from June through mid-September.

Mating occurs shortly after emergence, in April and early May, and the young are usually born from late July through September. A litter averages about ten babies, but only 20 percent of the newborns will survive their first year. Predators include various other snakes, raccoons, great blue herons and a variety of hawks and owls.

Juvenile Concho water snakes are particularly dependent on the shallow riffles in which they catch red shiners and bullhead minnows. Some have been found to disperse as much as two or three miles, but most wander no more than a quarter-mile along the river bank.

Early surveys suggested that the entire population of Concho water snakes might number no more than 330 to 600, and additional scientific studies were ordered under the provisions of the Endangered and Threatened Species Recovery Program. The Colorado River Municipal Water District has monitored the population since 1987, and several riffles were constructed along a seventeen-mile stretch of the Colorado River between the Robert Lee Dam and the town of Bronte in Coke County.

Water snakes now occupy those artificial riffles, and others have been found along the rocky shorelines of the E. V. Spence Reservoir and Ballinger Municipal Lake. Apparently there are many more than was first estimated.

The plight of the Concho water snake illustrates many of the problems involved in preserving endangered species, especially those that are difficult to monitor. Local politicians have long argued that protection of these unique Texas snakes is unnecessary, and that holding up lake construction is bureaucratic folly. Many have been strongly opposed to the ten-year study, an opinion that is not unexpected when financial interests are at stake.

Whatever the current population of the Concho and Brazos water snakes, however, their continued existence depends on preservation of suitable habitat. Construction of additional dams will inevitably result in the flooding of many miles along the few remaining free-flowing streams. As urban sprawl increases, pollution also threatens water quality. Petroleum production and processing, sewage disposal, pesticide use and feedlot activities have all been identified as major concerns.

A delicate balance exists between human needs and endangered-species management. Intelligent compromises are essential, but the two need not be mutually exclusive. Preserving habitat and maintaining water quality are as essential for our own future as they are for the Concho and Brazos water snakes and countless other wildlife species.

Piping Plover

Charadrius melodus

Snowy Plover

Charadrius alexandrinus

Least Tern

Sterna antillarum

In January, 1991, a team of biologists and volunteer birders launched an intensive ten-day census of piping plovers along the Texas Gulf Coast. Using airboats and all-terrain vehicles and hiking countless miles on foot, the group combed the beaches and tidal inlets in search of the small seven-inch birds. The final tally was 1,904 individuals, 35 percent of all the piping plovers remaining in the world and virtually the entire breeding population of the Great Plains.

"The survey once again emphasizes the importance of the Texas Coast to so many coastal avian species," wrote noted Texas bird authority Ted Eubanks, coordinator of the census and a member of the federal recovery team for the piping plover. "The reddish egret, whooping crane, piping plover, and the eastern subspecies of the snowy plover are examples of coastal species whose very existence in the United States may depend upon Texas coastal marshes, beaches, and tidal flats."

The piping plover breeds in several disjunct ranges on the Great Plains of the U.S. and southern Canada and on the upper Atlantic Coast. Both of these populations are listed as federally threatened. Another group in the Great Lakes region is classified as endangered. In winter the plovers move southward to the lower Atlantic and Gulf states. Because the northern breeding season is very short, birds begin arriving on the wintering grounds in late July and remain until April. Thus, although they do not breed in Texas, the coastline of our state is home to these seriously threatened little plovers for nine months of the year.

First depleted by hunting in the late 1800s, piping plovers now suffer primarily from destruction and alteration of their habitat. Sandy beaches on which they nest are giving way to residential and commercial developments along the coasts and around the Great Lakes. Construction of reservoirs and channelization of the rivers have affected long segments of the Missouri and the Platte in the Midwest, destroying countless sandbars on which the birds depend.

Snowy plover

Similar problems impact the little plovers on their wintering grounds in Texas. Recreational uses of the beach disturb feeding and roosting birds, and four-wheel-drive vehicles tear up the food-bearing substrate containing the marine worms, insects, crustaceans and mollusks that make up the bulk of their diet. The ever-present threat of oil spills also looms large as a potential hazard to the plovers and other coastal birds.

Pale, sandy tan on the back and head and white below, the piping plover matches the color of the dry beach sand that it prefers. In breeding plumage, a single narrow, dark band crosses the breast, although it is sometimes incomplete, especially on the female. The breast band is lacking in winter plumage. Bright orange-yellow legs distinguish the piping plover from the slightly smaller snowy plover, which always has dark legs.

Like others of its family, the piping plover is a chunky, compact bird with a short, thick neck and large eyes. It is a visual feeder, running quickly across the beach or the algal mats that line tidal mudflats, stopping to pick at tasty morsels with its short, pigeonlike beak. Then it darts off again—stop and start, stop and start—looking very much like a tiny wind-up toy.

The snowy plover, *Charadrius alexandrinus,* which often shares the piping plover's winter habitat, also faces an uncertain future. It, too, was counted during the 1991 piping-plover census, and the total barely exceeded 1,400 individuals. "That is a paltry sum if one considers that the coast of Texas (and the northern Gulf Coast of Mexico) is the center of the eastern snowy plover s wintering range, said Eubanks. Circumstantial evidence indicates that the snowy plover may be in greater danger of extinction in the United States than the piping plover.

Nor are these small plovers the only threatened birds to utilize Texas beaches. Pretty little least terns, *Sterna antillarum*, nest in scattered colonies all along the Gulf and Atlantic Coasts and through the midsection of the country. Many of the colonies are declining dramatically, and the interior subspecies was listed as endangered in 1985.

Plume hunters nearly exterminated these smallest of our terns before legal protection was obtained in 1913. The feathers, and even whole birds, decorated women s hats, and an estimated 100,000 birds were shot annually at the turn of the century. Although recovering from that onslaught, the least tern now suffers from the same loss of habitat that places the small plovers in peril.

Coastal colonies occupy sandy beaches, the females laying their two speckled eggs directly on the sand or among scattered shells. With continued residential development, dogs and cats have become major predators along our shores. Fishermen and beach-goers, too, disturb the colonies and keep the birds from their nests while eggs and young perish in the blazing sun. Automobiles and foot traffic take their toll of eggs that are perfectly camouflaged against the shifting sands.

Endangered interior least terns breed sparingly along the Canadian and Red Rivers in northern Texas and in isolated spots along the Rio Grande. Here they face an overwhelming alteration of their habitat, as do others of their race that nest on inland river banks and sandbars through the midsection of the country.

Least tern

Interior least terns join their coastal relatives on Texas beaches during migration, for all populations wing southward to spend the winter months in Central and South America. During their stops to rest and feed, they share the shore with piping and snowy plovers and a host of other avian species that all depend on this vital yet fragile habitat.

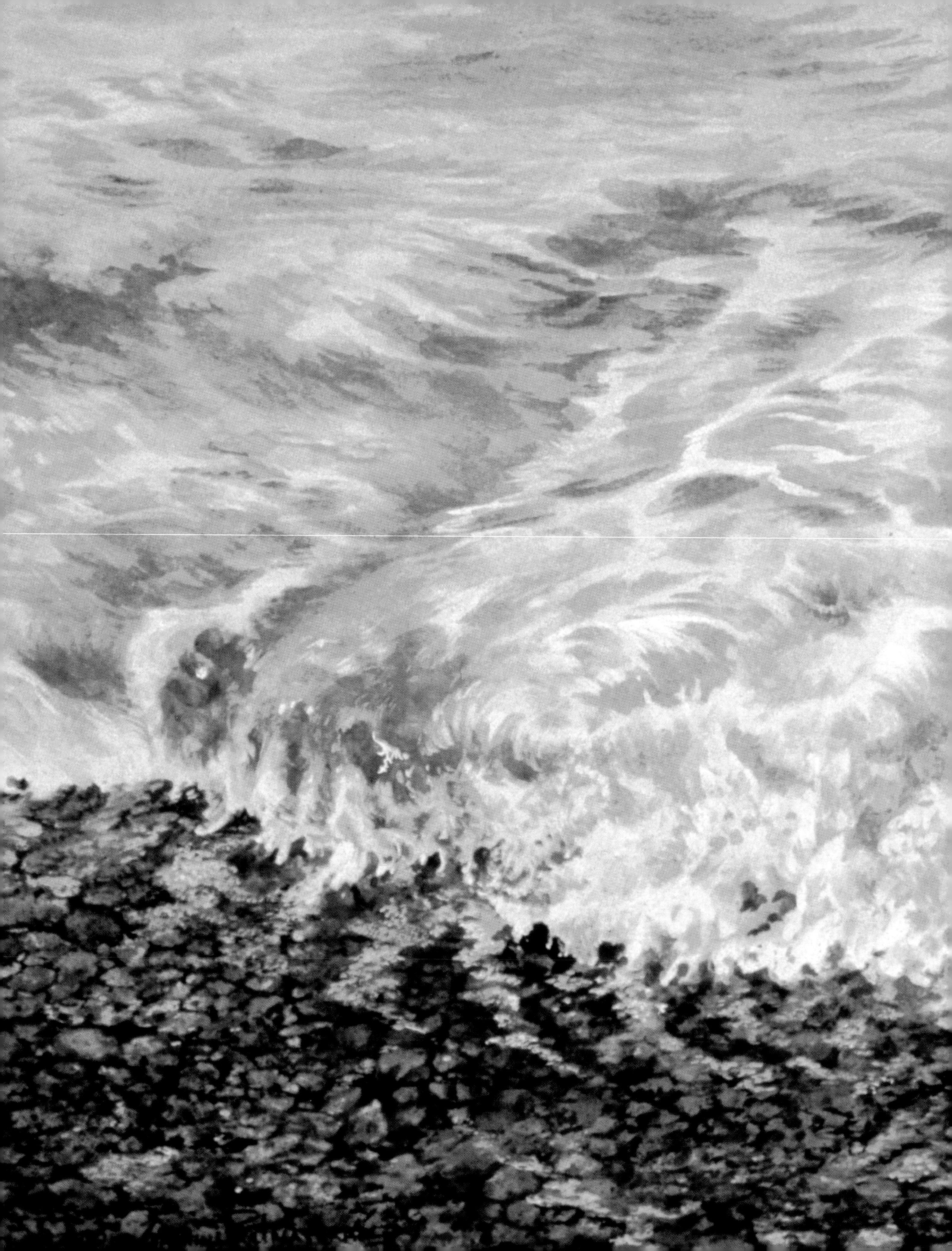

Greater Long-Nosed Bat

Leptonycteris nivalis

The midsummer sun sinks toward the Window framing the western edge of Big Bend's Chisos Mountains, and long shadows creep across the mile-high Basin. Bird songs begin to fade as darkness approaches, and hummingbirds steal one more quick drink from the blooms that dot the rugged, rocky slopes.

Then, as the moon rises above the shoulder of flat-topped Casa Grande Peak and the chant of the poorwill fills the air, other wings flicker across the evening sky. Ghostly shapes swirl around the tall flower stalks of century plants, replacing smaller hummingbirds that fed there through the day.

These creatures of the night are greater long-nosed bats, one of the rarest of more than thirty bat species found in Texas. Attracted to new blossoms that open only to the darkness, they drink deeply of the abundant nectar, spreading pollen as they move from plant to plant.

Indeed, plant and bat have apparently evolved together, and each is dependent on the other. Nectar and pollen of the century plant, or agave, constitute the major foods of the long-nosed bat during its summer sojourn in the Trans-Pecos. The bat, in turn, transports pollen stuck to its fur and apparently serves as the major pollinator of the agave.

Also called the Mexican long-nosed bat, this rare mammal was discovered in Texas in 1937 and has been reported only from the Big Bend region of Brewster County and from the Chinati Mountains in neighboring Presidio

County. The only known colony within the state is in a large cave hidden high on the slopes of Mt. Emory in Big Bend National Park.

A Mexican species, the greater long-nosed bat apparently breeds south of the Rio Grande and gives birth to one, or perhaps two, young during April, May and early June. Females then migrate northward with their offspring, arriving in our state as the agaves burst into full bloom. Few males have been recorded from Texas, suggesting that these bats may segregate by sex after breeding, most males remaining farther south throughout the year.

From June into August, when the flowers are at their peak, the bats course the night skies above Big Bend, hovering on strong, leathery wings to feed, gradually weaning their young within the sheltering confines of the cave. Then, as the agaves wither and die, the bats move back across the border, feeding on a variety of tropical flowers through the long winter months.

The population of the Emory Peak colony fluctuates wildly from year to year, sometimes numbering more than 13,000, sometimes falling almost to zero. Reasons for this fluctuation remain unknown, although it seems likely that the bats move northward to Texas in larger numbers when food is scarce in Mexico.

In spite of the wide variation, it appears that the overall population is slowly dwindling. Large Mexican colonies that once contained more than 10,000 bats are gone; others become smaller every year. As with other bat species, disturbance of roosts in old mines and caves leads to abandonment or to decreased breeding success. The constant clearing of range lands also decreases available habitat and food supplies.

The greater long-nosed bat was added to the federal list of endangered species on September 30, 1988, and the Mexican government followed suit with a similar listing in May of 1991. The species also occupies a place on the Texas endangered species list.

A relatively large bat compared to most of the species found in our state, the long-nosed bat has a characteristic elongated muzzle tipped with a distinct nasal leaf. The long tongue can be extended as much as three inches and bears hairlike projections that aid in lapping nectar as the bat hovers at deep-throated flowers.

Although the greater long-nosed bat occupies a unique ecological niche in Texas, it is by no means the state's only threatened bat species. The spotted bat that also occurs only in the Big Bend region, the southern yellow bat of the lower Rio Grande Valley, and Rafinesque's big-eared bat of far East Texas all share the dubious distinction. Others are classified as threatened or endangered in various regions of the country.

Only in recent years has the public come to appreciate the vital role of bats in our environment. Thanks in large part to the efforts of Dr. Merlin Tuttle and Bat Conservation International, a nonprofit group headquartered in Austin, Texas, we now realize the good these flying mammals do. Texas' huge colonies of free-tailed bats consume enormous quantities of harmful insects, and some have now become major tourist attractions.

Each bat species has its own niche to fill; each is important in its own way. Sharing the Emory Peak cave with the greater long-nosed bats, for example, is a colony of Townsend's big-eared bats. While the former emerge at night to sip nectar from agaves and pollinate those desert plants, the latter scour the skies for insect prey.

Texas Kangaroo Rat

Dipodomys elator

Palo Duro Mouse

Peromyscus truei comanche

Texas kangaroo rat

Much has been written about the plight of our larger threatened and endangered mammals. Wild cats, wolves and bears face an uncertain future, but many small animals also share that dubious distinction. Several of North America's rodent species are equally in peril and deserve special consideration and protection. Most occur over a very small range or occupy highly specialized habitats that are subject to human interference. Among these we count the charming little Texas kangaroo rat and the Palo Duro mouse, both of which are included on the official state list of threatened species.

The Texas kangaroo rat, *Dipodomys elator*, is known only from a few counties in north-central Texas and the extreme southwestern corner of Oklahoma. There it inhabits areas of clay soil with short, sparse grasses and small, scattered mesquite bushes. No other type of habitat seems suited to its needs.

A beautiful little animal, it closely resembles several other kangaroo rats that range across the more arid regions of Texas and throughout the deserts and plains of the western states. Its buffy brown upperparts are sparingly washed with black, while the underparts are white. The long, tufted tail is tipped with white and serves as an aid in balancing.

Like others of its family, the Texas kangaroo rat scurries about on all fours when foraging, but is capable of spectacular leaps on unusually long, powerful hind legs when alarmed. It bounds along at an amazing rate, its long tail streaming out behind.

According to Davis and Schmidly in *The Mammals of Texas*, the entrance to the underground burrow of the Texas kangaroo rat is invariably located at the base of a small mesquite, one of the mesquite roots often forming the top or side of the opening. Unlike most other kangaroo rats, however, *elator* does not plug the entrance during daylight hours to control temperature and humidity.

Almost entirely nocturnal, it waits until complete darkness to emerge from its burrow, and it reportedly forgoes feeding forays on bright, moonlit nights.

The Texas kangaroo rat feeds on the seeds and leaves of grasses and other low plants, carrying food in fur-lined cheek pouches and storing it in underground chambers of the multi-roomed burrow system. According to some studies, the seeds of cultivated oats and Johnsongrass form a major portion of the rodent's diet. As with many other closely related kangaroo rats and pocket mice, its body manufactures water from the food it eats, and it therefore has little need to drink.

Evidence indicates the Texas kangaroo rat may breed throughout the year. There is a peak in reproductive activity in early spring and another in late summer, and the young develop so rapidly that babies born during the spring may bear their own litters later that same year.

With so rapid a reproductive system, one might think that the Texas kangaroo rat could succeed against all odds. Such is not the case, however. The primary threat appears to be the clearing of the mesquite on which this fascinating little animal depends. This is one more case where loss of habitat poses a serious threat to the preservation of a unique wildlife species.

The Palo Duro mouse inhabits an even smaller and more specialized habitat along the caprock at the eastern edge of the Texas High Plains. There it can be found sparingly in the Palo Duro Canyon region of Armstrong, Briscoe and Randall Counties, from which it takes its name.

The taxonomy of this unique Texas mouse has long confused mammalogists. A member of the genus that contains the more familiar white-footed and deer mice, it was first described as a new species in 1943 and given the scientific name *Peromyscus comanche*. Later it was thought to be a subspecies of the rock mouse. Finally, in 1972, a detailed genetic examination proved it to be markedly different from the rock mouse and more closely allied with the widely distributed pinyon mouse, *P. truei*. For that reason, it has again been reclassified as a subspecies of the latter and bears the name *P. truei comanche*.

Tawny brown above and white below, the Palo Duro mouse has a long, distinctly bicolored tail that equals or exceeds the length of the head and body combined. It also has the very large ears that characterize the nominate subspecies of the pinyon mouse.

Although little is known about its habits, it probably feeds on both insects and plant material during the summer months and on seeds and juniper berries through the winter. Breeding habits are likewise poorly known, according to Davis and Schmidly.

Rocky canyon slopes dotted with juniper and mesquite trees seem to be the principal habitat of the Palo Duro mouse, but live-trapping experiments indicate a very low population even in such regions. This unique Texas mammal faces a precarious future as juniper forests are cut and human activities encroach even on the caprock canyons.

Louisiana Pine Snake

Pituophis melanoleucas ruthveni

While snakes may not share the wide popular approval accorded birds or mammals, they are nonetheless fascinating creatures that play important roles in the amazingly intricate web of life. Many inhabit specific environmental niches that define their range and are declining dramatically as those habitats vanish in the wake of human intrusion.

One of the rarest snakes in all of North America is the Louisiana pine snake, which occurs only in west-central Louisiana and the adjacent fringe of extreme East Texas. There it is limited to sandy, upland soils with stands of longleaf pine and bluestem grasses, a plant community that is disappearing rapidly across the southeastern states.

As the native pine woodlands and savannas give way to agricultural crops, pasturelands, tree farms and housing developments, countless plants and animals disappear as well. Sharing the range of the pine snake are the red-cockaded woodpecker and such unique

Texas wildflowers as the large-fruited sand verbena, white bladderpod and Texas trailing phlox. All are now included on the state list of endangered species.

The Louisiana pine snake is one of several subspecies of *Pituophis melanoleucas* that range across the continent from coast to coast. Eastern forms are called pine snakes; those of the Midwest and prairie states, including the western portions of Texas, are called bullsnakes; and those of the Far West are known as gopher snakes. All are large and bulky, but with surprisingly small heads for their body size. When disturbed, they hiss loudly and vibrate their tails. Although they may strike vigorously if approached too closely, they are not venomous and should not be feared.

Adult pine snakes attain an average length of four to five feet, and the verified record length is nearly six feet. Color varies dramatically, but most are buff to yellowish brown, with dark dorsal blotches that also vary from reddish brown to black. Those blotches are more distinct posteriorly as the ground color becomes lighter, and they usually form transverse bands across the tail.

Pituophis melanoleucas ruthveni, the Louisiana pine snake, feeds primarily on mice and rats and is an important agent in rodent control. It also shares its preferred habitat with Baird's pocket gopher, which serves not only as a prominent prey item but as a source of ready-made burrows. Left to its own devices, however, the pine snake is an accomplished burrower, and it normally seeks shelter underground. Except during the hottest weather, it hunts by day, seeking occasional lizards, amphibians and birds to supplement its rodent diet.

Pine snakes are egg layers, with small clutches of three to five leathery eggs. Those eggs range up to five inches in length, however, and may rank as the largest of any U.S. snake. The hatchlings are correspondingly large, sometimes reaching a length of twenty-two inches.

The Louisiana pine snake was first recognized as seriously threatened and given protection under Texas law in 1977. It is also under consideration for federal listing. Yet the real answer lies not in protecting just the snake, but in protecting the habitat to which it has adapted.

The same can be said for many other snakes across the state. Some, like the speckled racer, northern cat-eyed snake, black-striped snake, Texas scarlet snake and Texas indigo snake, are species that range sparingly northward from Mexico, occurring in Texas only in the lower Rio Grande Valley. It is a region filled with subtropical flora and fauna found nowhere else in the United States, but the unique thorn-scrub forest is rapidly vanishing to make way for more croplands and trailer parks.

Similarly specialized habitats are disappearing across other portions of the state, and with them the plants and animals that call them home. The Concho and Brazos water snakes and the smooth green, Big Bend blackhead, northern scarlet and Texas lyre snakes are all included on state lists of threatened and endangered species. The key to their future lies in saving their habitats, simultaneously preserving a host of other vanishing species that share the same environments. No creature exists in isolation. As early naturalist John Muir once noted, each thing in nature is attached to the rest of the world.

Karst Invertebrates

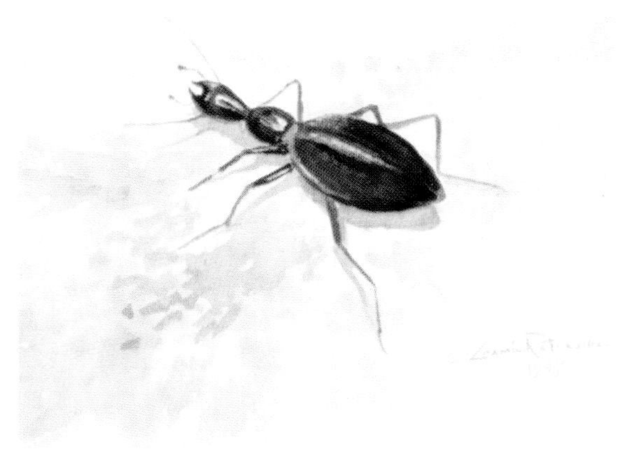
Tooth Cave ground beetle (*Rhadine persephone*)

Deep beneath the rocky hillsides near Austin, Texas, lies a patchwork complex of small limestone caves, some linked by narrow passageways. Access to the labyrinth is through small crevices and sinkholes flanked by busy roadways and residential subdivisions. No light penetrates the darkness of these subterranean hideaways; the humid air is cool and dank.

A small, reddish brown beetle no more than a quarter-inch long ambles slowly through the dark recesses of a cavern, digging in a layer of silt for the cave cricket eggs on which it feeds. Nearby, a tiny creature resembling a tailless scorpion is also on the prowl amid shelving rocks. Yet another niche contains a small, tangled spider web holding a minute, cream-colored spider. Its slender, sensitive legs grip the web, waiting patiently for food that its rudimentary eyes will never see.

All three of these strange creatures—the Tooth Cave ground beetle, Tooth Cave pseudoscorpion and Tooth Cave spider—spend their entire life underground. The former has been found only in Travis and Williamson Counties in Texas; the latter two are confined to Travis County. All are included among seven animals called "karst invertebrates" that occur in these two counties and are classified as "endangered" by both state and federal law.

Karst is a geological term used to describe a region of irregular limestone in which erosion has produced fissures, sinkholes, underground streams and caverns. Acidic groundwater percolating through the limestone slowly dissolved the calcium carbonate, creating the honeycomb formations. Many were originally filled with water, but as the water table dropped, ceilings collapsed, creating caves and cracks now open to the air.

Biologists believe that the ancestors of these tiny invertebrates moved into the underground niches during the Pleistocene, perhaps in search of a more stable environment. There they adapted to life in the darkness, gradually losing skin pigments and becoming lighter in color. Some now have no functional eyes at all; others retained rudimentary vision, perhaps discerning only light

Tooth Cave pseudoscorpion (*Tartarocreagris texana*)

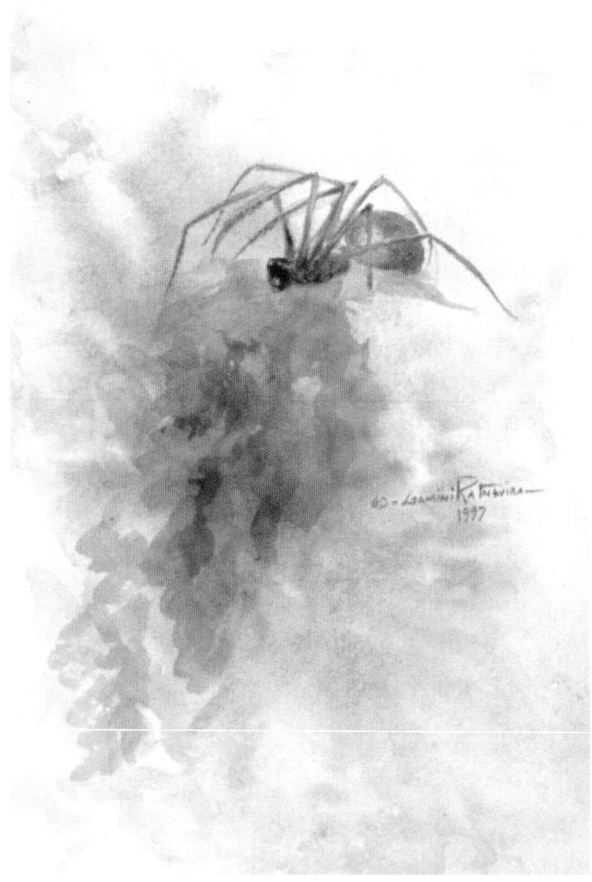

Tooth Cave spider (*Neoleptoneta myopica*)

and dark. Most have long, slender legs or antennae, substituting the sense of touch for their lost sight.

Subsequent geological faults and the continued down-cutting along stream channels carved the karst terrain along the Balcones Fault Zone into islands, with barriers that prohibit interbreeding among populations of the tiny cave inhabitants. Here on the eastern edge of the Texas Hill Country, isolated in their own strange environments, they further evolved into a series of distinct species.

Little is known of the habits of these rare invertebrates, but most are probably predators on even smaller insects and arthropods. They may also feed on decomposing organic matter swept into their chambers by subterranean streams. Adapted to constant temperatures and high humidity, they know no seasonal cycles.

Because there is no light for photosynthesis in the dark passageways, karst ecosystems depend on surface plant and animal communities for nutrients and energy. Leaf mulch and organic debris washes in with percolating water, while plant roots penetrate the bedrock. Ubiquitous cave crickets, too, play an essential role, roosting and laying eggs in the caves by day while feeding on the surface at night. Their eggs, nymphs and decaying remains provide a rich source of food for the predators and scavengers that cannot venture out themselves.

The three Tooth Cave invertebrates, along with the Bee Creek Cave harvestman and Kretschmarr Cave mold beetle, were declared endangered by the U.S. Fish and Wildlife Service on September 16, 1988. Later, two more tiny creatures, the Bone Cave harvestman and Coffin Cave mold beetle, were described after additional research and taxonomic splits. Because they had originally been classified as populations of the protected harvestman and mold beetle, they were automatically added to the list.

The decision was not popular on every front, especially in an area that has also seen campaigns for the protection of the endangered black-capped vireo and golden-cheeked warbler. The critical habitat is on the edge of the rapidly expanding Austin metropolitan area, and concern over pending construction projects runs at fever pitch. Requests by county commissioners to delist the karst invertebrates were filed and, after further studies and hearings, denied.

Most of the species in question inhabit formations near busy residential areas or commercial facilities. The threats are many. Additional construction could alter drainage patterns or cause collapse of the caves. Pollutants—including sewage, fertilizers and pesticides—could filter into the groundwater, poisoning everything in their path. Even human visitation has a deleterious effect, opening the humid caverns to dessicating air flow and disturbing sensitive substrates in which the invertebrates live.

No less a problem has been the introduction of the imported red fire ant, which has also been implicated in the loss of other wildlife. Not only are the ants potential predators of the protected species, but they compete for many of the same prey items.

These inhabitants of Travis and Williamson Counties are not alone in their predicament. Nine cave-dwelling invertebrates from Bexar County were proposed for listing in 1993, and three more beetles and amphipods from Comal and Hays Counties were nominated in 1995. Extensive research and lengthy hearings will determine the outcome, but politics will play a major role. Either decision will be met with heated opposition.

It is easy to find public support for the tiger or panda, for the majestic bald eagle and whooping crane. But the karst invertebrates are not cute or cuddly, nor are they particularly regal. Some of the tiny creatures are smaller than a single letter in their lengthy scientific names, and few people will ever meet them face to face. "What good is it?" and "Why do we need to preserve it?" are common questions. Should they, as has been said of many small animals, be accorded protection by "riding on the tail feathers of the bald eagle?"

The most obvious answer is that these species took millions of years to evolve and deserve a chance for survival. More practically, their loss is indicative of environmental problems that will eventually affect us all. As endangered-species coordinator Gerry Bade of the U.S. Fish and Wildlife Service said in defense of a similar tiny cave amphipod in Illinois, "You start knocking out the bricks on the bottom row, and things are going to start falling down."

Bone Cave harvestman (*Texella reyesi*)

Red-Cockaded Woodpecker

Picoides borealis

The charming little red-cockaded woodpecker inhabits open, parklike pine forests across the southeastern portions of the United States, ranging from North Carolina to Florida and sparingly westward to Texas. It is a local resident of the East Texas Piney Woods and shares that habitat with the tiny brown-headed nuthatch and Bachman's sparrow. All are prizes sought by birders from around the world, for each is restricted to this unique environment.

Only eight inches long, the red-cockaded woodpecker has a black-and-white barred back, a black cap and white cheeks that serve as the most distinctive field marks. The tiny red patches on the sides of the head, the cockades for which the species was named, are barely visible in the field. Downy and hairy woodpeckers also inhabit the pine forests of East Texas, but they can be distinguished from their much rarer compatriots by their white backs and black cheeks.

Unfortunately, the red-cockaded woodpecker has declined dramatically throughout its range and was first named to the federal and state lists of endangered species in 1970. It owes its precarious status to its highly specialized nesting habits, for it is the only woodpecker that excavates cavities exclusively in the heartwood of living pines, most of which are infected with red-heart disease. This fungal disease makes the tough heartwood softer and easier to work, but it occurs mainly in mature trees that are at least sixty to seventy years old. Modern forest management techniques, however, call for cutting mature stands of trees, and as a result, the woodpeckers have abandoned their nesting colonies throughout a major portion of their range.

Red-cockaded woodpeckers live in small family groups, or clans, that consist of a mated pair, their offspring of the year and occasional unmated male helpers. These colonies usually number from two to six birds, but some contain as many as nine. There is always, however, only one breeding pair. The young helpers assist with incubation of the eggs, which hatch in ten to twelve days, and feed the young that fledge about twenty-six days later. They also play an important role in constructing new nest cavities and defending the clan's territory.

The birds remain territorial throughout the year and reuse their homes year

after year. Each colony occupies a cluster of cavity trees that contain active holes, and each member normally roosts through the night in its own cavity. It may take several years of intermittent work to construct each new chamber in the living pines.

After making the nest cavity, the birds then drill small holes around the entrance to increase the flow of sap, and they pick at them frequently to keep them open. The sticky resin coats the trunk, marking the trees distinctively and helping to repel marauding snakes and other predators.

The major threat to the endangered red-cockaded woodpecker has been the dramatic decrease in old-growth pine forests. Present-day practices normally call for short-term timber rotation, much to the dismay of the trees' avian inhabitants. Fire suppression, too, has played a detrimental role, for the woodpeckers prefer a grassy understory with little brush, and they abandon their nest trees when small, crowded hardwoods and pine saplings reach the level of their cavities.

Infestations of the southern pine beetle are also of considerable concern. An epidemic following the devastation by Hurricane Alicia in 1983, for example, killed large areas of native pines in Texas' Sam Houston National Forest, displacing several woodpecker colonies.

Red-cockaded woodpeckers prefer to forage in living pines for the wood-boring insects and grubs that make up the bulk of their diet. Males feed primarily in the upper portions of the trees; females, along the lower trunks, thereby apportioning the food resources. As they troop through the woods, they can be located by the sounds of their tapping and by their nasal calls, a raspy *sripp* and a high-pitched *tsick*, quite unlike the notes of other woodpeckers within their range.

The vulnerability of this little woodpecker was dramatically demonstrated by Hurricane Hugo in 1989. At that time there were an estimated 2,000 active red-cockaded woodpecker colonies in the southeastern states, most of them in unlogged national forests. South Carolina's Francis Marion Forest contained 562 of those colonies when Hugo swept inland across the region, leveling 100,000 acres and destroying the cavity trees of more than half the resident colonies. Only one percent survived totally unscathed.

Many steps have been taken to preserve the red-cockaded woodpecker, and they have met with some success. In 1988 a federal judge in Texas ordered the U.S. Forest Service to stop clearcutting within 4,000 feet of colonies in the state, and all national forest units have reviewed their management policies.

Texas recovery efforts include several other programs. Corridors of continuous habitat are being planned to link widespread colonies and increase interaction and dispersal. Young woodpeckers have been captured and moved to augment small clans or single birds that remain outside the boundaries of established groups, and nest boxes have been inserted in mature pines as artificial cavities.

Surveys conducted throughout eastern Texas in 1996 counted about 900 woodpeckers in 316 colonies. Federal and state lands harbored a total of 271 groups of one to nine birds each on such tracts as Sam Houston, Davy Crockett, Angelina and Sabine National Forests; Alabama Creek, Bannister and Moore Plantation Wildlife Management Areas; Jones and Fairchild State Forests; the Alabama-Coushatta Indian Reservation; and the Big Thicket National Preserve. Forty-five more clans inhabit private lands belonging primarily to timber companies, and many of those companies have agreed to set aside areas for the preservation of the woodpeckers.

Given suitable habitat, the red-cockaded woodpecker can survive. Its persistence and perseverance are amply illustrated by a recent incident reported in the *Journal of Field Ornithology*. An established nest tree was cut illegally, dragged fifty feet, and partially buried under other logging debris, fortunately with the cavity still facing upward. When seen by a research team, the parent birds had worked their way through the overlying branches and continued to feed a surviving nestling. It eventually fledged to take its rightful place within the clan.

EXTIRPATED ANIMALS

Vast bison herds once covered the Texas prairies "like a black cloud," according to reports by early settlers. Scout and plainsman Billy Dixon, as quoted in Robin Doughty's *Wildlife and Man in Texas*, wrote that their sound came rolling from the plains, deep and moving, not unlike the rumbling of a distant train passing over a bridge. Camped along the Canadian River, Dixon recalled that "as far as the eye could reach, south, east and west of me there was a solid mass of buffalo—thousands upon thousands of them...."

Called "buffalo" or "wild oxen" by most early Texans, the American bison, *Bos bison*, was formerly widespread throughout much of Texas, avoiding only the dense forests of the Big Thicket. This, however, was only the fringe of a much more extensive range; an estimated 60 million bison once roamed North America.

The enormous herds spread from the Great Plains southeastward as far as Florida and the Carolinas and northward into Canada. Seasonally migratory, the huge animals, some weighing as much as a ton, plodded southward as winter threatened and returned north in spring. The bison has been called the "life of the Plains" and the "biological wealth of the frontier."

With the westward expansion of white settlers, however, the bison was exploited on an incredible scale. It was practically extinct east of the Mississippi by 1825, and the building of the transcontinental railroads threatened the western herds. Hundreds of thousands of bison were killed and left where they lay, hunters taking only their hides and tongues.

The last great slaughter of the southern herd occurred in Texas in 1877-78. At least 1,500 hunting teams worked out of Fort Griffin in Shackleford County, taking more than 100,000 hides in December and January alone.

When the Texas Legislature considered protecting the remaining bison, General Phil Sheridan opposed it, according to Davis and Schmidly in *The Mammals of Texas*. Sheridan pointed out that "the sooner the buffalo was eliminated the sooner the Indian would be starved into submission." His prediction quickly came true; by 1880, both were almost gone.

Incredibly, the enormous herds had vanished throughout the country. All that remained of the "life of the Plains" was a herd in Yellowstone National Park and a few privately owned animals. Those numbers have grown through the intervening decades with renewed interest in our wildlife heritage, and as many as 200,000 now range across numerous tracts of public and private land.

American bison

It is highly unlikely, however, that the bison will ever again be allowed to roam free. That point was emphasized in 1997, when hundreds of bison were shot by ranchers when they strayed out of Yellowstone Park in search of food. The animals were killed to prevent the spread of brucellosis to the ranchers' cattle, but not one case of such transmission has been documented.

More encouraging is the 1997 news from the Texas Parks and Wildlife Department that an "official Texas bison herd" is being moved to Caprock Canyons State Park near Quitaque in Briscoe County. The direct descendants of calves captured and cared for by pioneer rancher Colonel Charles Goodnight, the forty to fifty animals have been called the "purest-blooded bison left in North America," and have roamed the JA Ranch in the Texas Panhandle for more than 120 years.

It is fortunate that remnants of the great bison herds remain, if only in captivity, but such is not the case for other wildlife species that once inhabited our state. Many have vanished entirely, leaving only memories and museum specimens. Enormous flocks of passenger pigeons and Carolina parakeets once darkened the skies over Texas, while ivory-billed woodpeckers hammered away at virgin timber in deep East Texas and Eskimo curlews stopped on the coastal prairies during their long migration flights between the Arctic tundra and wintering grounds in Argentina. The pigeon and parakeet passed into oblivion in the early 1900s; the woodpecker and curlew apparently followed more recently.

The passenger pigeon, *Ectopistes migratorius*, was the most abundant bird in the world during the early days of our country's history. Ornithologist Alexander Wilson estimated that one flight contained two billion birds, while John James Audubon watched a single flock pass overhead for three days and estimated that at times as many as 300 million pigeons flew past in one hour.

Texas shared in this avian bounty. One hunter brought down eighty-seven birds with one blast from his shotgun, while a farmer in Wise County in 1870 reported that enormous numbers of pigeons congregated to roost in the evening, and large trees toppled under their combined weight.

Somewhat larger than the common mourning dove, the passenger pigeon was slim and elegant, with a blue back and rosy pink breast. It was a valuable food source for early settlers, and no one could imagine the eventual extinction of the species. It came with amazing rapidity, however. A single Michigan market hunter shipped 3 million birds in 1878; eleven years later, the species was extirpated in that state. By 1900, the passenger pigeon was gone from the wild in Texas and the nation, shot for sport and for its meat. The last known individual, a female named Martha, died at the Cincinnati Zoo in 1914, and what was once this planet's most numerous bird was extinct.

The Carolina parakeet, *Conuropsis carolinensis*, also swarmed across the countryside, ranging from Nebraska to New York and southward to Florida and the Gulf States. It was a fairly common summer resident in North Texas, and occasionally occurred as far south as Corpus Christi.

Unfortunately, the little parakeets were fond of fruits, nuts, corn and other crops and swarmed over grain until, in Audubon's words, they looked like "a brilliantly coloured carpet." Farmers shot them relentlessly, and many were captured as cage birds. By the early 1900s they, too, were gone. The last Carolina parakeet died in the Cincinnati Zoo in 1914, ironically mirroring the

Passenger pigeon

demise of the passenger pigeon.

Reports of ivory-billed woodpeckers, *Campephilus principalis*, continue to emerge from the river-bottom forests of East Texas, but most are undoubtedly due to confusion with the still-common pileated woodpecker. There have been no unequivocal sightings of the huge ivory-bill since the 1950s, and most authorities now consider it extinct.

Few could have foretold the ultimate extinction of the vast bison herds, the enormous flocks of passenger pigeons and Carolina parakeets or even the reclusive ivory-billed woodpecker. Without adequate protection and preservation of all-important wildlife habitat, however, others are sure to follow.

Ivory-billed woodpecker

AFTERWORD

What can Texans do to preserve wildlife diversity, protect wilderness and reverse the trend of habitat deterioration in the Lone Star State?

Partnerships between communities and businesses need to provide win-win solutions and improve resource use. Competing uses can become complementary with creative thinking and enterprise. Forums can be established in which public agencies, citizens and industries recognize success and redirect activities where necessary, thereby involving the community in assessing and monitoring the health of the ecosystem.

Urban areas can potentially provide important opportunities for wildlife enhancement. Some city planners are developing wildlife environments in metropolitan areas. City parks and open spaces can provide habitats for migratory and resident birds. Simple, inexpensive measures to conserve and increase biological diversity include reducing the frequency of mowing along highways and cutting and pruning vegetation after the peak breeding season for birds. We can stop the use of herbicide spraying on roadsides, forests, and other areas to control vegetation. Highways and roadways can be planned to minimize interference with migratory pathways, making roadways "wildlife friendly." We can address the effects of urbanization; restore native habitats in natural areas, green belts, and parks; and create Texas "wildscapes" by turning our own backyards into better wildlife habitat.

Learn about endangered species living in your region and work to ensure their survival. Find out their habitat requirements and what you can do to increase habitat diversity. Do not use pesticides and herbicides. If you have gardens, check organic gardening literature for safer control methods. Set up "safe disposal" systems for existing toxic materials. Recycling efforts can be intensified; recycle paper and use only recycled paper products to reduce cutting of trees. Do not burn leaves; start a compost pile to return the nutrients to the soil. Give up your gas-powered lawnmower. With imagination and foresight, urban and suburban landscapes can become stepping stones to the environmental health of our planet.

By planning and working together, we can continue to advance and sustainably develop as a civilization, while protecting our natural environment for future generations. There are some success stories. The bald eagle was once endangered but is now off the endangered list because so many people worked together to help save it. Scientists first looked at all the reasons the eagles were dying out, then wildlife biologists, lawmakers and citizens worked together toward solutions that saved our national bird from extinction.

In spite of such successes, however, more critical habitat is being lost than ever before, and a record number of species are being recommended for the threatened and endangered list.

Habitat fragmentation is occurring rapidly as urban development expands into rural and suburban areas. Large land holdings are being subdivided by construction of roads, boundary fences, and utility easements.

Encroaching development destroys valuable wetlands as well, decreasing nature's ability to deal with flooding by replacing absorbent earth with hard building surfaces. In addition, wetlands destruction reduces available environment for wildlife, a major cause of declining numbers of many species.

As human populations continue to grow, resource managers must develop technologies to restore and maintain habitat fragments and find ways of linking habitats along common corridors. Restoration implies restoring former important habitat types that may be under-represented in the system and that may provide refuge for various nongame wildlife species not previously considered in management plans for a particular site. Working together, biologists and landowners can find ways to help keep species from dying out. Successful plans include setting aside special areas for native species in order to save them from extinction, eliminating the use of certain pesticides and herbicides in farming and ranching, and managing livestock production in ways that also protect rare species and preserve wildlife areas.

Wildlife corridors are natural areas linking together critical habitats. These green regions are surveyed and set aside for the purpose of connecting already existing wildlife refuges and wilderness areas. Without appreciably affecting general land use, diverse gene pools of indigenous flora and fauna can be connected with an eye toward preserving wildlife species now in an extinction spiral. These green pathways can be seeded with native herbs, grasses and wildflowers and reforested with a diversity of aboriginal trees.

Preservation of our remaining wilderness has been facilitated by organizations such as The Nature Conservancy of Texas, the Audubon Society and many local citizens' groups. Studies are being undertaken to ascertain the most effective way of preserving nongame, endangered and threatened species, including invertebrates and plants. This research reflects an important objective of recognizing how every animal is supported by the interrelated web of vegetation, soil, and climate that provides the environment for life. Resulting surveys of declining biota are leading to the development of plans and teams of specialists to save them.

Joint efforts can allow particularly sensitive areas to be protected forever. For example, Christmas Bay, the pristine location of the last of Galveston's coastal sea grasses, has already been designated a Texas Coastal Preserve. Similar steps were taken for Armand Bayou. Both projects were partnership actions by the Galveston Bay Estuary Program, the Texas Parks and Wildlife Department, the Texas Natural Resource Conservation Commission and the General Land Office. Wildlife refuges and preserves are an essential way to protect and save threatened and endangered species and habitats.

The Caddo Lake Institute was formed as a foundation underwritten by Don Henley, a noted American musician-environmentalist. The role of the Institute is to act as an "ecosystem-specific" sponsoring entity, underwriting local wetland science and conservation education, as well as cultural and ecological research and monitoring. The Institute, in partnership with federal and state conservation agencies, created an initiative that resulted in the designation of approximately 3,300 hectares of land under the Ramsar Convention of Wetlands of International Importance.

Recognized as one of Texas' most important and unique inland freshwater wetlands, Caddo Lake provides significant and regionally critical habitat for a variety of migratory and resident wildlife species.

More and more informed citizens, scientists and educators are willing to address the problems of disappearing species by seeking to understand the critical needs of native animals, especially certain long-neglected nongame species, in order to establish guidelines that will make wildlife conservation a component in plans for our state's future.

However, additional efforts must be made to increase the nongame and endangered species conservation fund, which has seen severe budget limitations. Write to Texas Parks & Wildlife (TP&W) and ask what you can do individually to further habitat restoration. Texas nongame wildlife species received some tangible benefits during the past decade, ranging from songbird roosts to bat caves. With use of these special funds, TP&W can build on dozens of research projects that are now being conducted in the state, such as current research on mountain lion population and distribution in south Texas, monarch butterfly migration, habitat used by neotropical birds in the Rio Grande Valley, population status of the peregrine falcon in the Trans-Pecos, and the effects of grazing on the protected habitat of the threatened Texas tortoise. Several sites have already been acquired, and others are being reviewed for acquisition opportunities. The fund is also working with the Texas Private Lands Initiative and The Nature Conservancy of Texas to restore native flora in areas of the lower Rio Grande Valley where habitat has been lost by clearing.

We can build support for nongame and endangered species through cooperation and education, and we can build good working relationships with private landowners as well. For example, the Partners in Flight Initiative, a songbird conservation program, utilizes partnerships among researchers, conservation groups, landowners, birders, and the general public to actively pursue conservation of migratory birds and their dwindling habitats. Through this and other conservation initiatives, land managers are encouraged to assess the impact of their management practices on species shown to be declining.

Texas is unique among our fifty states because 97 percent of the land is privately owned. Efforts to protect, preserve or restore endangered species and habitats are futile without a strong commitment from private landholders. Numerous options are available to landowners that will allow for the preservation and protection of the special qualities of their property.

Land trusts are local, state or regional nonprofit organizations directly involved in protecting land for its natural, recreational, scenic, historical or productive value. They have varying conservation objectives—some work in specific geographic areas or concentrate on protecting different natural or cultural features. Land trusts are a creative answer to today's land conservation challenges. They offer a flexible, cooperative and effective approach to land conservation.

Where the Edwards Plateau, the Chihuahuan Desert and the Rio Grande Plain brushland biological regions converge, they create a landscape of striking beauty and diversity. The Nature Conservancy of Texas began a land trust on 18,500 acres, called the Dolan Falls Preserve. The preserve's canyons support stands of oaks and sycamores bounded by steep cliffs dotted with scrub juniper and mesquite. Black-capped vireos and other rare and endangered species such as the Texas snowbell and Mexican white oak are found on the tract where the Devil's River is replenished by freshwater springs flowing from the bases of towering limestone cliffs. This and other riparian corridors in the region serve as important migration paths for birds and other wildlife in the arid West. To achieve the goal of perpetual protection of the land, the Conservancy's management plans have been developed to provide long term stewardship for the property and its inhabitants.

Private land stewardship can ensure the perpetuation of wildlife habitat primarily through sustainable agricultural practices that allow us to produce our food without damaging the land. As Will Rogers once said, "They're makin' people every day, but they ain't makin' any more dirt."

Organic foods are produced under a system of ecological management that relies on building humus levels in the soil through crop rotation, recycling organic wastes, applying balanced mineral supplements and using crop varieties resistant to disease and pests.

Farmers are now learning that organic techniques are good business. Not only are organic foods more in demand at the market, but farmers save money by not using chemicals. Each year millions of pounds of pesticides costing hundreds of millions of dollars are applied to crops in Texas. Farmers and scientists are finding that organic farming produces as much food as chemically intensive farming.

Farmers, ranchers, agency biologists, and agricultural specialists working together can resolve problems between endangered species conservation and private land uses. Many farmers and ranchers these days practice some form of conservation, but earlier abuses resulted in the loss of large areas of native grasses. Overgrazing has left a legacy of degradation. When carefully controlled, grazing can aid in the enhancement of wildlife habitat. Intense overgrazing and failed attempts at brush control have resulted in dominance of large areas of rangeland by dense brush and thorny plants.

Some ranchers are finding that the benefits of a holistic resource management system far surpass their expectations. In some cases, infestations of alien flora have been countered by methods that simulate those historically determined by large herds of bison, along with reintroduction of important species that kept invading flora balanced before overgrazing altered the ecosystem. Indigenous plants return as the range heals itself through proper management.

Woodlands have been substantially altered over time as well. Pre-Colonial old-growth forests and many indigenous species are reduced in number; some are gone entirely. Creation of pastures and tree plantations has strongly affected wildlife habitats. If we control use and development, attempt to leave old growth, and promote industrial responsibility, then sound land husbandry can restore native flora and fauna.

Conservation Biology, a conceptual approach to conservation and management that emerged in the early 1980s, is defined as the maintenance of biological diversity. Besides broadening the species perspectives of management agencies, conservation biologists have emphasized the importance of genetic diversity, sustainable resource management, and the maintenance of ecological and co-evolutionary processes in conserving natural communities. Traditional wildlife management approaches have not placed enough importance on the total biological diversity of a region, focusing almost exclusively on a select few game species. Conventional approaches often focus primarily on specific short-term results with less understanding and/or awareness of long-term implications. This approach keeps us in a crisis-management or reactive mode versus a more proactive forward-planning mode.

Within the context of a holistic approach, ecosystem processes, human dynamics, and finances are all important when considering the issue of stewardship. Economic and ecological sustainability are not diametrically opposed. We must continue to use new and innovative approaches in order to move conservation and protection of our environment away from political theory to the realm of practice. If future generations are to have the opportunity to experience the natural wonders that previous generations have taken for granted, society must work toward a change of values. Our children have to live and cope with the consequences of the environmental neglect past generations have wrought. It is essential that we prepare them for this critical task.

Finally, it is absolutely essential that we awaken in young people a sense that they have the power to make a difference. Currently, many of our children grow up feeling that the environmental problems we face are too large, too difficult and thus hopeless. A critical part of any environmental education program must be an emphasis on individual empowerment. Young people can and must help to make this world a better place for themselves and for generations to come.

Endangered Species Media Project
Frank Salzhandler

Epilogue

Wilderness, wildlife and sealife diversity in Texas is a gift beyond measure. Maintaining natural habitats is a central conservation concern. The health of other species is a strong indicator of the health of the habitat we share with them. Human existence depends critically on the quality and diversity of life. Our success as a species is based on the ability to utilize biological diversity for food, clothing, medicine, and shelter. Biologists know that today's accelerated decline of wildlife results from habitat degradation. According to the National Science Foundation, "We are rapidly running out of time where we can hope to understand and preserve the diversity of life on this planet."

Native plants and animals, and the balances of nature that keep wildlife and humans healthy, are pushed a little farther off-center with each species we lose, every wild acre we destroy, and every stream we contaminate. Public and private landholders must understand that what they do affects people and areas far away. If our state's wilderness areas are overgrazed or denuded of trees, water tables throughout the region are destroyed and floods take place many miles away.

Our state's wildlife and sealife, like our air and oceans, are not owned by man, though they are used by virtually all Texans. Individual citizens and governments must share in stewardship efforts to protect and conserve these resources. The economic value of our wildlife environment extends far beyond its commercial value. Each year millions of people enjoy Texas' natural heritage for outdoor recreation: hiking, backpacking, camping, swimming, boating and bird watching on nature trails, in parks, refuges, wildlife corridors and open spaces.

From the springs and rivers of the Trans-Pecos and the Edwards Plateau to the bayous and lakes of the Big Thicket and the Coastal Plains, Texans must look at wildlife habitats in terms of nature's wonders to be preserved for generations to come, rather than simply as building sites for real estate developers and construction companies or open sewers for easy use by industries and cities. The overwhelming mandate from the people in Texas must be to recognize and to protect our remaining natural heritage from callous disregard of the public interest.

Pride in our state's natural heritage and an increasing sensitivity to the future quality of our environment have become virtues of the Texas character, but action and endowment is limited. Budgetary constraints and staff limitations have curtailed the work and quantity of research directed at many nongame and endangered species programs for the Lone Star State. Efforts to expand regulations governing habitat destruction and to encourage protection of predatory and nongame animals have met with mixed results.

Texans want wildlife corridors and wilderness trails. Texans want clean waterways and coastlines. Texans who share the passion for conservation of the richness of our state's natural environment are numerous. We must make our numbers count by continuing to stand up for this crucial cause. Though we have not yet won the battle, our voices are beginning to be heard.

ESMP/F.S.

The Artist

Gamini Ratnavira continually contributes to the international art scene by creating images that reflect his experiences as a conservationist, scholar and expedition leader. His work has been exhibited with numerous tours, including the Endangered Species Media Project's "Images of Vanishing Nature" show and "A Brush with Nature." Gamini continues to exhibit one-man shows across the United States and internationally. He is now working on other books featuring tropical birds of the world, in addition to his work in the *Vanishing Wildlife of Texas* publication and museum tour.

The Authors

John and Gloria Tveten are nature writers, photographers and lecturers and have collaborated on numerous books on natural history. These include *The Birds of Texas*, *Wildflowers of Houston and Southeast Texas* and *Butterflies of Houston and Southeast Texas*. Their articles and photos have also appeared in hundreds of other books and magazines, including publications by the National Geographic Society, Time-Life, the National Wildlife Federation and the National Audubon Society. Their weekly newspaper column, "Nature Trails," has appeared in the *Houston Chronicle* since 1975.

THE ENDANGERED SPECIES MEDIA PROJECT is a non-profit corporation chartered by its founders in 1989 to promote greater understanding of how the quality of human life can be enhanced by the preservation of our wilderness and wildlife, and to promote imaginative support for the advancement of a greater ethic concerning the Earth's ecology.

In execution of its purpose, the Endangered Species Media Project focuses its activities on the following areas:

- *To encourage and promote artists and educators that foster a thoughtful perspective toward the stewardship of our Earth's treasures.*
- *To initiate and support programs that provide hands-on ecological activities for young people; inspiring and involving them, for positive change toward their future.*
- *To create and produce conservation programs for literary, artistic, inspirational and educational purposes.*

The Endangered Species Media Project exists as a cooperative partnership between educational and private sectors.